More Tales from the Igloo

As Told by Agnes Nanogak
Introduction by Robin Gedalof McGrath

Hurtig Publishers
Edmonton

Hurtig Publishers Ltd.
10560 – 105 Street
Edmonton, Alberta
Canada T5H 2W7

Canadian Cataloguing in Publication Data

Nanogak, Agnès.
  More tales from the igloo

  ISBN 0-88830-301-7
  1. Inuit — Legends.*   2. Legends — Arctic
regions.   I. Title.
E99.E7N35   1986   398.2′097   C86-091290-6

Printed and bound in Canada

Contents

III — Tales of Sorrow and Revenge

Foreword

These stories from Agnes Nanogak have survived almost one hundred years of social and cultural upheaval in the Canadian Western Arctic. Prior to 1890, when American ships began wintering over at Herschel Island, contact between the Mackenzie Inuit and outsiders was rare; each subsequent spring a huge fleet would gather to hunt whales in the waters north of the Mackenzie Delta. These ships brought with them men from all over the world; Europeans, Asians, Figians, and Eskimos from Alaska, and the men brought alcohol and disease that almost wiped out the native population. The first decades of the twentieth century saw rapid change on the Arctic coast. The whaling industry failed, only to be superseded by the trade in Arctic fox and muskrat; the introduction of guns and steel traps decimated the animal population; and measles, smallpox, and tuberculosis wiped out entire native villages. Missionaries, Mounties, and traders came in increasing numbers, each determined to salvage souls, lives, and profit from the growing chaos.

In the midst of this turmoil, Agnes Nanogak was born, the daughter of an Alaskan Eskimo and a Copper Inuit. Nanogak's father, William Natkutsiak, better known as Billy Banksland, came into Canada as companion and guide to the explorer Vilhjalmur Stefansson in 1911; her mother, Topsy Ikiunak, came from farther east but grew up with the Mackenzie people. They lived around Baillie Island until

Nanogak was fourteen, and in 1939 they moved to the Holman area. That year, Father Henri Tardi established a Catholic mission at Holman and families began to settle around the new Hudson's Bay trading post built the following year. Agnes Nanogak married Wallace Kunak Goose in 1943 and, like most Holman Inuit, lived a semi-nomadic life that included time spent on the land and in the small settlement. Kunak's grandmother, Mannie Mumyok, was an important part of the young couple's life and she taught her protégé many of the skills and stories that Nanogak later handed on to her own seven children.

By 1960, fur trapping in the Arctic had declined and was no longer a major source of cash for Canadian Inuit, and Father Tardi began to look for other ways to help his people earn a living. The success of the Cape Dorset print shop, under the direction of James Houston, encouraged him to suggest printmaking as a viable alternative to trapping, and in 1961 the Holman Co-operative was formed to retail the output. Nanogak, who had been encouraged to draw at a very young age by her father, soon became involved. Her graphic art, rooted as it was in a vast knowledge of Inuit myth and legend, showed a lively confidence that ensured her inclusion in dozens of exhibits, and eventually she began having shows of her own.

Nanogak's storytelling background and illustrative expertise were widely recognized in 1972 when she produced the visual interpretations for *Tales From the Igloo,* an anthology of legends collected by Father Maurice Metayer. The thirty-one drawings in the book gave a unity of voice to the six Copper Inuit storytellers included in the volume, but the text did not draw directly on Nanogak's own wide knowledge of Inuit narrative. A 1976 film, *The Owl Who Married a Goose,* was Nanogak's first chance to tell one of her own stories to a non-Inuit audience. The legend, animated by Caroline Leaf, won eight awards including an Oscar nomination. This volume, for the first time, presents Agnes Nanogak as both storyteller and illustrator.

The storyteller's art is a complex one. It must be both entertaining and didactic; it must amuse the listeners but it must also give them food for thought. Inuit myths and legends, with their lively characters, blood-curdling events and unpredictable endings, certainly capture the imagination, but they also serve a serious function. They concern themselves with universal subjects such as man's relationship with nature, his fear of death, his need to order society and to be accepted into it. The stories Nanogak tells here are not concerned with the creation of the cosmos or the religious beliefs of her people, they are concerned with the problems of everyday life, they are legends that have some basis in historical facts and events.

Inuit legends fall into a number of categories, but by far the most easily recognized are the beast fables or animal stories that open the collection. In these beast fables the animals act like humans, they can talk and wear clothing or even be transformed into human shape, but they also retain some of their animal characteristics. The owl still gets sleepy in the sun and the wolves are still voracious. By centring the story on a beast or animal, the storyteller is able to generalize the figures and to free them from the demands of reality so that they can have unlikely adventures. Using animals in this way also creates a comic distance which allows people to laugh at themselves and at their own failings.

Inuit storytellers are all very fond of beast fables which involve animal-spouses, and Nanogak has included a number of these later in the collection. Animal-spouse stories usually involve a transformation from human to animal form; the animal character is often a faithful wife or a providing husband, but the human character is overly-critical or dissatisfied. It is only when the animal-spouse runs away that the human realizes the true value of the relationship. Sometimes, through magic, humans in these stories are briefly turned into caribou or birds. When they regain their natural form, they have usually learned something about themselves through their experiences. The transformation marks the movement from childhood to maturity, and the acceptance of adult responsibility.

Many of Nanogak's animal stories have a moral, although this may not be readily apparent to non-Inuit. For example, variations of the story of the whale which transformed itself into a young man and was killed is known across the Arctic. Sometimes when Nanogak tells one of the variants, the story ends with both the murderer and his wife aging suddenly, as a punishment not for the infidelity or the murder, but because they deny knowledge of the bowhead's death to its parents. Nanogak says "When my father would tell us this story as children, he would say, 'I am telling you this to teach you not to lie, for all the things you do in secret, they come undone'."

The second section of this book is made up of tales of epic heroes. Unlike the epics of classical literature, Inuit epics don't usually have

a national or patriotic importance, but they do have supernatural beings who involve themselves in the fate of a principal character who
has a great many adventures in different settings. Heroes are vital to
every society because they provide people with examples of realistic
men and women who, almost incidentally, have magical powers or
extraordinary qualities. Like Achilles and Ulysses, Nanogak's Inuit
heroes are restless, aggressive, death-defying characters who would
probably be uncomfortable people to live with but who are fascinat-
ing to read about.

Elements of both the beast fable and the epic can be found in the
stories in the third section of this book. Here we also find cautionary
tales, designed to illustrate the consequences of bad behaviour, and
accounts of violence that goes unpunished. Inuit society values self-
control and co-operation to a high degree, so that anger, greed or
selfishness that causes murder and elicits revenge is the subject of
serious disapproval. In a society where murder is abhorred and for-
mal war is unknown, real-life incidents of violence are not quickly
forgotten. In these stories, justice does not always prevail, the good
are not rewarded, and the wicked are not punished. What we see is
communal suffering and a continuation of bad feelings right into the
second and third generation. The lesson is that undesirable behaviour inevitably leads to a disruption of the social order and the
suffering of innocent people.

One aspect of Inuit legend that causes some trouble for people
brought up outside the tradition is the occasional absence of a re-
demptive or happy ending. For example, one story here tells about

a cannibalistic squirrel-woman whose victim escapes and returns to his wife and children. When the creature pursues him, his real spouse transforms into a bear, but paradoxically the bear loses the battle with the squirrel and even the children are killed. Nanogak, like most Inuit storytellers, often breaks the happy-ending rule and presents us with a universe that is not just impersonal but is downright malevolent. The fact is that life in the Arctic, even today, is fraught with hazards and dangers. A sudden drop in temperature can turn a family outing into tragedy within hours, a loose dog can tear a child to pieces in moments, life is fragile and often unfair. The nightmare elements in these stories reflect the different experiences and the different values Inuit have from their countrymen to the south.

In the old days, these stories were not written down in English but were told aloud in Inuktitut in the igloos, tents, and cabins that were strung out along the Beaufort Sea. In the winter darkness, the sea ice formed and buckled into high pressure ridges, turning the ocean into a highway fractured with icy barriers. By dogteam and on foot, the Inuit travelled along the coast. In the short summer months, the Mackenzie thawed, pouring the waters of half a continent out past the pingos and mountains into the Arctic Ocean where *umiaks* and schooners hurried between Herschel and Holman. Trade goods and furs, children and lovers, were exchanged on these trips, cementing the bonds between the Alaskan and the Copper people who were moving towards each other, filling the spaces left by the tragic decimation of the Mackenzie Eskimos. Stories, too, were exchanged, traded by men waiting patiently for game, whispered between sweethearts on the sleeping platforms of tiny shelters, transmitted by elders to hungry or fractious children, offered between women engaged in preparing skins or food.

Inuit storytellers used more than words to convey their tales; they inserted songs, wove string figures, made faces, performed dances, and drew pictures, all to make the giants and trolls more frightening, to make the heroes more handsome and brave, to describe better the terror of the child snatched by ghosts or the dismay of the owl tricked out of his dinner. Scraps of hide were cut into fantastic shapes. Fingers were dabbed in lamp soot and drawn across igloo walls. Tools of ivory were decorated with magical themes such as shamans turning into bears or spirit-women becoming birds. Bits of antler or stone were carved into the beasts and beings that people the stories. Even the land itself became an easel, and young girls would smooth a patch of mud or snow and take up the storyknives their fathers had made and draw the things they told about.

It is from this tradition that Agnes Nanogak comes, a tradition which has always used illustration as a key to communication. The stories published here were painstakingly translated by Billy Goose, Nanogak's son, and by Annie Goose, her daughter-in-law, yet each step away from the original Inuktitut distances us. Nanogak's illustrations help to draw us closer again, pulling us into the magical world where animals wear parkas and owls eat off plates, where kayakers paddle across the sky, a world peopled with cranky trolls and kindly giants, drum-dancing fish and boys who turn into weasels. With her varied background and her illustrative skill, Nanogak truly represents all the storytellers of the Western Arctic. She represents the Alaskan Eskimos who came to visit and stayed to settle, the Copper Inuit who travelled from the coast and the islands into the delta, and the Mackenzie people who died in the settlements of Kittigazuit and Shingle Point, Tununuk and Kendall Island, Inuit who live now only through their stories, through Agnes Nanogak's words and pictures.

Robin Gedalof McGrath
September 1986

I Tales of Birds and Beasts

Siksik, the Squirrel

Siksik, the squirrel, came out of her den early one day. It was going to be a very warm day, so Siksik was going to go pick berries.

While she was picking berries, Okpik, the owl, flew down and frightened Siksik very much. She tried to go inside her den, but she could not fit easily through the opening, because all summer long she had been eating so many berries that she was too fat.

So Siksik told Okpik to wait outside her den and that only when the sun went down could Okpik eat her up. Okpik was very happy because Siksik had no way to get away now. She started to believe Siksik, who told her, "Okpik, you can see I could not get away from you. I will even pick berries for you while I am waiting."

Okpik started to feel sleepy standing in the warm sun. Soon she fell asleep, and then Siksik jumped past her to her den. Siksik had almost squeezed through the opening, when Okpik woke up and caught the end of Siksik's tail, and tore it off.

Siksik told her children, "Ask for my tail from Okpik; say, 'Please give back our mother's tail.'" She told her children to give Okpik something to eat. What they threw to her was really a hard stone. Okpik opened her mouth and bit the stone, thinking it was something to eat. Her beak broke because she had bitten so hard on the stone, and she was hurt and crying, "Siksik has fooled me; I am dying."

Soon Okpik died, and the children got back the end of their mother's tail, and mended Siksik's tail. Her tail soon healed and she and her children lived happily, always.

Avingalok, the Lemming Sister and Brother

Two lemmings, who were brother and sister, were going to go across the river. It was a long way, but finally they reached the other side of the river. As they shook the water off their fur, they saw a man's footprints on the mud. They could see that the footprints came from a house on a hill nearby. The lemmings were both very tired from their long swim. They went to the house and when they got there, they found two plates of akootok (Eskimo ice cream), so they started eating it, and finished their meal.

They heard someone coming outside. "Where will we hide?" they cried. The lemmings had just managed to hide when the owl who lived in the house came in and asked one plate, "Who emptied you?" The plate answered back, saying, "The two that came from far away." The owl asked the second plate, "Who emptied you?" The second plate answered the same way. "Where did they hide?" the owl said, and looked all over, turning everything over. When he found the lemmings, he swallowed them whole.

The two lemmings were very frightened, but they had carried a knife with them, so they were able to cut their way out of the owl's stomach. When they finally came out, they laughed with joy.

Toktovak, the Moose

One summer day, Toktovak, the moose, was near a lake where there were many mosquitoes. Just across the lake was a man. It was very hot, but Toktovak was galloping back and forth to try to free himself of all the mosquitoes. In the end, Toktovak plunged into the lake to swim towards the other side. As soon as he reached the opposite shore, the man started towards the moose so that he could kill him. A little while later, the man had caught up with the moose. The moose turned to the man and asked, "How will you kill me?" The man said, "With my knife." The moose said, "No, the knife is too cold." The man said, "Then I will kill you with my harpoon." "No," the moose said again, "the harpoon is too sharp." But the man did kill him with the harpoon and brought the moose home for his wife to cut up the meat and dry the skin.

While the wife was cutting up the moose, it began to speak to her, asking, "What will you do with my skin?" The wife said, "I will dry it up and then we will use you for our blanket." The moose said, "No, your children will get it dirty. Do not use me for your blanket." When she started cutting the meat before drying it, part of the moose meat said, "Won't you cook anything? You should cook a meal for your family." So the woman said, "I will cook." Soon a meal was boiling, and the family ate.

The wife put the moose skin to dry in the sun, stretching it out on the ground. When it was dry, they wanted to use it for a blanket. When night came, they went to bed, using the moose skin as their new blanket. Just as they were about to fall asleep, the moose skin began to talk again, waking them up every time they began to fall asleep. Finally, the man got tired of the moose that talked so much, even though it was just a skin. He got up, tore the moose skin to pieces, and threw it out. Finally, the moose stopped talking, and everything was peaceful again.

Tologalok, The Old Crow

Tologalok the crow lived all by himself. One day a wolf came by, and Tologalok said to the wolf, "Let's go sliding down the high hill." Then Tologalok began to slide. He kept sliding for a long time, telling the wolf, "You should try sliding, it is so much fun!" Each time the wolf would refuse, but in the end Tologalok's words were too tempting for the wolf, so the wolf started to slide down the hill. He came down very fast, and when he reached the bottom of the hill he crashed and was knocked out.

Tologalok came down the hill and skinned the wolf, went home, set out the cooking pot, and started cooking supper. Soon a pack of wolves came and said, "We have tracked down one of the members of our pack. His tracks end here. Do you know the wolf we mean or have you seen a wolf around here?" "No," said Tologalok, "I have not seen anyone around here, but I caught a bull caribou and it is just about done cooking. Why don't you all take your parkas off and have supper with me?" So the pack of wolves took their parkas off and came in to wait for supper. Then Tologalok said, "I have to go out for a little while. I'll be right back." He ran out and collected all the wolves' parkas and hid them all and then went back inside and started serving his guests supper. The wolves said, as they ate, "This meat tastes like and smells like wolf meat. It is like eating our own selves." "No," said Tologalok, "It is a bull caribou I killed. Eat your supper."

Tologalok waited until they had all finished. Then he flew out of the window and started laughing, at the same time saying, "You have eaten your own kind!" All the wolves ran outside, when they realized they had been fooled. But they started to freeze because they had no parkas on. They looked for their parkas but could not find them. Soon they all froze to death. Tologalok had plenty of meat for a long time and he was dancing for joy.

NANOQAK

Toligak, The Sandpiper

Toligak and his sister were trying very hard to make a living. They had a tent camp all alone by themselves.

One day the male Toligak went hunting for ptarmigans with snares. These snares are made with string set in a certain way; when the ptarmigan steps in a snare, the string tightens up and you have caught whatever you are hunting. Soon, Toligak had got enough ptarmigans and then he had to pack them all the way home.

The sister Toligak was expecting her brother soon and was watching for him. She spotted him coming home from afar. She made a song while she was waiting because she was so happy that they would have enough to eat. The song she made said that the ptarmigan had very beautiful feathers, with very beautiful patterns of colours.

When her brother returned, she made a supper of ptarmigan for both of them and they had enough to eat and were both thankful.

II Tales of Adventure

A Man Called Konnak

Once there were some people who lived at the mouth of a river. They hunted seals during summer, waiting for the fall, when they would hunt caribou for their food. Soon some of the people went inland to hunt caribou, while the rest of the people stayed back at the camp near the sea. It was fall weather and the ice was starting to form on the smaller lakes. It was getting cold. To keep their tents warm, and also for cooking their meals, they needed to keep their seal-oil lamps lighted, but they were running out of seal oil. So they sent a young boy back to the camp to fetch some oil.

The boy left with his dogs. It was about one night's journey to the river camp, and he arrived at the next nightfall. He camped in an old igloo. The people who had stayed behind at the river had just recently left the camp, just before he arrived. Their igloo was still a bit warm, so he brought in a fish to thaw it out a bit before having it for his supper. After he had his meal he lay down to rest, thinking about who had first stayed in the igloo in which he was camping.

While he was lying there thinking, all of a sudden he heard a voice saying his name, "Konnak!" and at the same time something rolled down the side of the igloo, coming down slowly to the porch. "I stood up very fast," Konnak later recalled. "I could hear someone in pain, cries of suffering coming from the porch. I could hear two people out there. I was afraid. I could hear a child cry once in a while, and each time the child cried a fire flared up."

A woman with her hair covering her face slowly came through the porch entrance, crawling very slowly on her knees, a baby on her back. Each time the child cried, fire came out of the mother's hood. The woman came through the doorway and stopped. The man told her to come in, but she did not want to come in at first. The seal-oil lamp flickered; sometimes it almost blew out. Finally the woman started inside, still on her knees. The man said, "Don't let your baby cry."

He told the woman to have some of the frozen fish he had brought in earlier. He threw the fish over to her, but the fish flew right back at him. It was swimming in the air, even though it was a frozen fish!

As the man and the woman talked, she settled down and the baby stopped crying. All at once the woman rushed out of the igloo, all aflame. Then she rushed back inside, looking for the man. The man Konnak had run away along a trail, leaving all his dogs behind. The instant he saw the figure of fire come chasing him from behind, he ran as fast as he could go.

Early the next morning, still just ahead of the fire, he found himself near a camp. A man at the camp had got up early in the morning and had come outside to empty a pot. Just as the fire was about to overtake the boy, Konnak yelled. The man heard him and emptied his pot onto the fire and it went out. Konnak went over to the woman, who now lay on the ground barely moving. This woman had died in labour with the baby she had on her back, and the baby had turned into an evil spirit. That evil spirit was what had nearly killed Konnak. Now the people placed the baby in the back of the woman's parka and put her in the graveyard where she could rest peacefully.

Atangana and the Giants

Long ago a giant couple lived in a far-away place in the mountains. They were husband and wife, and the giant husband was very strong. One day a man called Atangana was hunting nearby and he came to where these two giants were living all by themselves. Taking the giant husband by surprise, Atangana killed him.

The giant wife was very angry, so she started to run after the man who had killed her husband. She chased Atangana to a river, which was too deep for him to cross. But he drank up the river water to make it shallow enough to walk across, and as soon as he could, he started across. When he reached the other side he heard the giant woman calling out to him, "Hey! How did you get across the river? It's so deep!" He told her, "You have to drink the water and make it shallow so you can cross over." So she stooped down and started to drink the water until she got tired and stopped for a while. But he told her, "Only a little more to go and it will be just right for you to cross over." So she stooped down again and drank some more water, but soon she burst because she had drunk too much water. The air became foggy because she had been so hot inside and she had drunk so much water.

Atangana started out again, and soon he came to a river where a group of people lived. When he came up to them along the bank, they asked him, "Where did you come from?" He told them he came from the mountains inland. "I had to kill this giant. I did not want to kill him, but he would have stopped me, so I had to kill him." The people did not seem angry. "Oh yes," they said, "when there was a caribou-hunting party up there, they found a giant human footprint, and there was no sign of caribou around that hunting ground. Now there seems to be another giant in another part of this land," they continued, "but this one is a very kind giant. He is the most helpful person." Sometimes when people were climbing hills, this giant would grab them and put them higher up on the hill, saving them the climb; and he would move all their belongings up higher too. Sometimes he would hunt seals for these people; he would wade in the water and catch hold of the seals as they surfaced for air. When the people went hunting by kayak, if they wanted to hunt somewhere else, the giant would take hold of their kayak and move them to a new hunting place, gently putting them down on new waters. This giant was very popular among the people. In winter, the giant slept, underwater. All winter long he would sleep, until the next thaw.

A short time later Atangana said he was going to travel to Point Barrow. When he reached there he stayed for some time and married a woman from there. This woman had many shaman spirits. When children were sick, she would do her shaman dances and heal these sick children.

One day there was to be a drum dance, and the people said to Atangana, "Come to this drum dance. You and your wife are invited." So they joined the crowd in the big tent. Atangana said, "I will go in the middle of the floor as soon as the music starts." As soon as the music started, he lay down in the middle of the floor, and they cut off his head! Then all the lights were turned out. But when they put the lights back on, Atangana was dancing in the middle of the floor with his head back on, for he had a shaman spirit. The people were amazed at his power.

Then Atangana told them, "Now take my wife Kinogana and tie her up very tightly. Secure the ends of the rope by having someone hold onto each end, and turn off all the lights." So the people did as he said, and they turned off every light. Soon they heard something like a dog barking, so they turned all the lights back on. There was Kinogana in the middle of the floor and she had no rope around her. Someone said, "You have some soot on your face. How did it get there?" Kinogana told them she had been going out the stovepipe, but then she realized that she had to come back in to show them how powerful she was, that she could be tied up and come out all untied again.

Now another person wanted to show her shaman power. She said, "Me, I don't have to have the lights out. You will watch me as I do my shaman spirit." She was tied up, in the middle of the floor. She struggled and started trying to fly. Soon she was flying free in the tent full of people. Then she flew outside and went way up in the sky.

After this competition of shaman spirits, Atangana and his wife Kinogana left the camp. They lived together, travelling around and hunting. But Kinogana got very sick and could not be made better. Soon she died. Atangana suffered at the loss of his wife. He would go hunting just to keep busy, and he would travel around, but he could not get over his wife's death.

One day he came across a giant who asked him, "Why are you so sad?" He told the giant about his loss, and he was invited to stay at the giant's camp for awhile. After a long time the giant told him, "It is time you got yourself another wife. It is not good that you mourn for so long. Look, there are women your age here and they are good workers and would make good wives." So Atangana chose himself a wife and they lived together; he found her very kind.

When Atangana went caribou-hunting he visited the giant who had encouraged him in his time of need. Atangana said to him, "Maybe you too should find someone to share your life with you, someone to cook your meals and sew clothing for you."

The giant agreed, so Atangana went to look for a wife for the giant. Atangana was looking for a girl from around his own home to be a wife for the giant, and he soon found a young girl who had learned the ways of making a home. He brought her to the giant's home. She liked the giant and the giant liked her, so he took her for his wife. Atangana said, "Because you always helped me, I helped you back in return."

But one day the giant could not find his wife. That morning he had rolled up his sealskin blanket without realizing that his wife was still sleeping inside, and when he sat on the blanket he smothered her. The giant suffered a great deal over the loss of his wife, for he had loved her very much.

Some visitors came and they were surprised to see him mourn.

They asked him, "Why are you so sad?" He told them, "I rolled up the blanket after I got up and I did not know my wife was still sleeping inside it. I sat on her without knowing and now she is dead. That is why I am mourning; this is a great loss to me."

Atangana tried to comfort the giant. He told him, "You must eat and try to get over your grief. You cannot go on mourning. You must eat or you will get weak. When I suffered you helped me and you must now listen to me." But the giant was so sad he could not even sleep. So Atangana stayed with him. In those days many people had lice and the giant was no exception. Atangana would pick lice off the giant's head. The giant was so big that his lice were the size of lemmings, and Atangana was very much afraid of the lice. But because he was a friend to the giant he would take the lice off the giant's head. Gradually the giant returned to his normal self, and started to get happy again. There was nothing else he could do.

Atangana was then free to go walking out on the land. There were many, many mosquitoes around, so he quickly got some water from a pond and then climbed a hill to look around. Down near the water he saw something very shiny and reddish, so he went down to pick some of this out of the rock. With his knife he carved out a piece of something very shiny and hard. He thought he would take it home to make tools such as knives or to use as nails. As he was going home, he came across two caribou, which he killed. He cached most of the meat but brought some of the meat to his friend, the giant.

He showed the giant the shiny rock he had found. "That shiny rock is found up near the large lake," the giant said to him. "When the sun goes over it the rock shines bright, and all this rock is around the banks of the river nearby."

Atangana went home to his wife, but next day he got ready to go out again, saying to her, "Let us go and get the caribou meat that I left up there inland, and at the same time we will go and look for this shiny rock that I was told about by this friend of mine. He said it is near the banks of the river. He had always wanted to go to this place, but he never reached it. He got old before he could go, because it is so very far inland and he could not go on such a long trip."

Then Atangana's wife's brother told him, "Let's go towards Utkalo (Baily Island)." When they reached it, they found a lot of their people there and so they stayed for some time. The men spent a lot of time gambling. Atangana was always winning and he cleaned out all his wife's brothers.

They got so angry at him that they started to think of killing him. When Atangana and his brothers-in-law were out hunting one day, the oldest plotted to kill him. When Atangana was not looking, the brother-in-law pulled out his bow and arrow, ready to kill him. Just before the brother-in-law loosed the arrow, Atangana turned around. "What are you aiming at?" he asked. His brother-in-law answered, "A ptarmigan landed beside you. I was going to shoot it, but it flew away."

But Atangana had a feeling that his brother-in-law had been aiming to kill him, so he started to take great care that he was always behind his brother-in-law. Soon they had lots of seals. They returned home and got ready to cut up the seals.

Just as Atangana and his wife were having tea in their tent, someone appeared in their doorway. He came in very slowly. The wife realized that it was her brother come to kill her husband. She ran in front of her husband to protect him, but her brother's arrow went through her body and through her husband's body and killed them both.

The man ran out, saying, "I killed my brother-in-law," and Atangana's sister came running up the hill crying for her brother.

Atangana's sister had a dog that she kept in her tent and which she always fed when she had her meals. She was still crying for her brother later in the evening when she went to bed, and she suddenly realized that her dog was staring at her. She asked, "Why are you staring at me?" Her dog tapped the ground and pulled off his hood. His face became human. "You think you are having sorrows, but you people don't realize how many problems we dogs have when our masters mistreat us, sometimes beating us until our bones are sore, or when we have to sleep outside in a blizzard. Sometimes we must travel and pull heavy loads and get very tired. You human beings think you suffer, but we dogs, we have the hardest lives. Now I will put my hood back on and return to my normal self." Then the dog pulled his hood back on and turned back into a dog.

So the girl pulled herself together and resumed her life. She told her mother how her dog had talked to her and told her of all the mistreatment dogs receive from their masters. She talked to the man who most abused his dogs and he never beat his dogs again.

The Old Couple Who Caught a Baby

Two old people, a man and his wife, set a fish net out in the water near the shore at their camp. They had nobody to help them, since they had no children, and it was very rainy. One day when the weather cleared they went to check their fish net. They had netted some fish, but a little further down the line there was a baby, a newborn baby boy. The old couple wanted to keep it, but at the same time they were afraid that it may have been placed there by someone, so they shoved it back in the water.

Not long after, the couple were visited by a number of families, which camped near their home. One family in particular had lots of children, and could not make ends meet. The parents could not provide food and clothing for all their children. Some were mistreated, because there were just too many for the parents to handle.

The old couple said, "Maybe we can raise one child for you, and when he is older you can take him back." So the old couple took one child and raised him and he grew to be a smart boy. The old couple told him never to answer back to people around him.

One day he heard about some strange people who lived nearby. The children were always told by their parents never to go near that camp, because they were very mean people and these strange people would eat human beings. Anyone who got close to their camp never returned home; they were always captured and killed. So the boy's stepfather talked seriously to him, giving him this advice: "Don't ever go near the camp. They have always managed to kill hunters even smarter than you, so if they ever capture you, you would have no chance."

Many years passed. Then one day the young man said, "I should like to see what it is like at the strangers' camp." So his stepfather said to him, "If you really want to go, please take my knife and my kayak and my equipment." The old woman said to her husband, "I hope our boy is safe and I hope he returns back home. If he is not attacked by a large group he will survive, but if they try to attack him in large numbers, he will not survive."

Later in the day the young man reached a camp, but the couple living there were normal people. They offered him a meal, and he ate with them. They told him this: "Those people over at that camp are very dangerous. When families visit our camp, those people always scare them away or else entice them over to that camp. But the families never return here nor do we ever see them again." Nevertheless, the young man set out early in the morning towards the camp.

In that camp, the most dangerous man was called Enagalik (Tilted Head). He wrestled with every person who was caught near his camp, and he always defeated his opponents.

When the young man arrived, a boy came up to him and said, "Could you come over to our camp for a visit?" So he went over to visit. As he walked into the tent, he saw a whale bone there with a big hole in it, and then Enagalik was upon him. They started to wrestle. The young man had to fight with all of his might and strength, but in the end he killed the man Enagalik by striking his head against the whalebone. His head rolled off onto the floor.

All the people cheered for the young man, because now they no longer had to be afraid. The young man said, "Was there anyone else who helped Enagalik?" The people said, "There was his wife and another man," the people said, so the young man killed them as well. He asked again, "Who else helped that man?" Again there was an answer: "He had two polar bears out on the ice as his helpers." So the boy went out to the ice. He came face to face with the two polar bears and told them, "We will run a race. Whoever is last will be torn apart by one of you." So the three started their race. Now out on the ice were five breathing-holes of bearded seals. The young man was running as fast as he could; quickly he went down the first breathing-hole and then came up by the fifth hole and ran towards a big house up on the shore. He ran inside. He found another polar bear inside. Just then the other two polar bears he was racing came in. He said to the third polar bear, "Tear up these two polar bears; they are evil."

In this way, he killed everyone who had helped Enagalik, the dangerous man. The people thanked him, saying, "We will never be afraid again."

As the young man was walking home he came across an old lady, who said, "My grandson is looking along the shoreline for anything that might be washed up on shore, for little fish or shrimps...." So he began to follow the grandson. He heard the grandson singing as he walked, and every time the grandson found fish and shrimps he

would eat every piece he found. Soon the grandson was so full his belly was large. He went home then and said to his grandmother, "I am very thirsty. What can I drink?" His grandmother said, "Out in back of the tent is a little pond. Go have some water from there." The grandson went out and, stooping down, started to drink the water. Soon the pond was empty. By now the boy's stomach was very large from all the fish and shrimps he had eaten and all the water he had drunk. He said to his grandmother, "I am very cold. Please put the stove on." So the grandmother put the stove on. Soon the fire was burning strongly. One ember flew out from the stove and landed on the grandson's belly and his belly burst and the grandson died. Seeing that she could not do anything about her grandson's death, after a while the grandmother left with the young man returning home from the camp.

They travelled along the shore by boat. Along the way they came across a man who was chopping the ground with an axe, and each time he struck the ground the winds roared. That's how blizzards were created. So the boy from the camp took the axe and ran away with it as fast as he could. When he was far enough away to be safe from the man, he broke the axe in half, so the man would no longer have a tool to create the winds. But the man chased the boy all the way to his home. The man looked through the window and begged the parents, "Please make your boy return my axe." But the boy answered for them, "I broke your axe because we are tired of the winds you created," so the man had to go away without the axe, and he was very sad.

A Young Boy Called Akakapangan

An orphan boy called Akakapangan lived with his grandmother among a lot of people. Most of the people did not care for them, except for one wealthy couple. The boy's grandmother made him some special gloves, and she taught him to be aware of dangerous ways. She told him to be very helpful to people around him.

The river where the people did their hunting was not far from their camp, but there came a time that when hunters left for the river they did not return home. One evening, when they were all gathered together in the large tent, the wealthy man said, "Why is it that when the hunters go towards the river, they don't return home? I wonder what the reason is?" So the young boy said, "I think I will go see why they don't come home." The wealthy man said, "My wife will cook you a meal before you go, and she will pack some muktuk, and dried meat, dried fish, and other provisions for your trip."

Akakapangan left on his journey. He headed along the narrow part of the river. Ducks flew as he got closer to them with his kayak. As he travelled, he would stop when he got hungry to have his meal. On his way he got a seal, and took along half the meat; then he got a caribou and he also took half of the meat. Then he came to a house, and he thought, "Maybe this is the house of the people who don't return home."

He had brought along the special gloves that his grandmother

had made for him, and he put them on. He waited inside for someone to come to the house. Soon something was coming; he waited.
The creature got closer and closer; still Akakapangan waited patiently. The creature came right up to the house and asked,
"Akakapangan, what are you doing here?" He called Akakapangan
by name, and Akakapangan was surprised. "Now how did he know
my name?" he wondered. I have never seen him before.

Meanwhile the creature was talking again, "I will swallow you
up whole like I did the others." Akakapangan looked around inside
the house and he saw some ducks there, so he took them and ran
to the doorway and threw them to the creature. The creature grabbed
them and started to chew on them. When he had finished them he
asked for more. "Or else I will swallow you whole," he said. So
Akakapangan again looked around for something. He saw three
caribou haunches, and he threw these out to the creature one at a
time, and each time the man chewed it up and ate the meat. Then
Akakapangan threw half of a seal carcass and said, "Here, fight it!"
The creature and the seal fought, but not for very long. In no time
the creature had chewed the seal up. But the fight had weakened him
a little; he had lost some of his strength.

Then Akakapangan said his same words back to him, something
like this: "I'm Akakapangan. You have reached me, and if you don't
give me something, I will surely eat you alive." The creature charged
at the house. As he came up to the porch, the boy thrust his harpoon
right through the creature's chest. The creature immediately took off
at a run outside. Akakapangan held onto the line of his harpoon for

a while, but then he lost his grip and ran out after the creature. He could see the creature running, never stopping, going over the hills and through the valleys with the spear of the harpoon stuck in his chest. He kept chasing the creature.

The creature ran into an old house, so Akakapangan, the orphan boy, ran into another house to wait for the creature to come out. In this house two very old women were sitting across from each other, making sinews to use as sewing thread. He took the parka of one of them and put it on, and he pretended to be an old woman too and sat down to make sinew thread. He said, "I would like to see the end of that creature who ate all those people." One of the old women said, "We would like to see him come to an end too. He frightens people and never lets them return home." The other old woman said to him, "We would like to help you make an end of him! What can we do?"

Akakapangan went to the hosue where the creature was hiding and peeked inside. He saw the rope of his harpoon. He looked closer and he saw the creature rolling around in pain. He told the people around him, "When I turn out the lamp I want you to all start singing a song. And when I say to stop singing, I will put the lamp back on. Then we will see what happens to him." So they did what he said. They sang when he put out the lamp. He went in the house and pushed the spear further in the creature. Then he said to the people, "Stop singing! I will see what happens now." He lit the lamp, and he saw that the creature seemed a lot weaker. He said again, "Sing some more." So the people obeyed. Again he turned the lamp out, and went inside the house, then told them to stop singing, and lit the lamp.

Akakapangan tried to check on the creature. All at once beside him a brown bear roared. The boy got so scared he ran away as fast as he could, but the brown bear ran after him. As Akakapangan ran he said to the ground, "Please hide me from the brown bear." But the ground did not reply. Soon some wolves joined the chase after him, along with the brown bear. He was getting tired, but was too scared to stop. He hid for a while behind a rock to rest. He peeked over the top of the rock and saw the wolves and the bear getting closer, still looking for him. They were furious and were talking very angrily.

So Akakapangan got up, and started sneaking from rock to rock until he was close to his kayak. Then he ran as fast as he could down to the river bank. When he was almost at his kayak, he turned around to the wolves and the bear and shouted to them, "I killed the creature because he killed all the people who went hunting near the river and left a lot of widows and orphans back home. So I took revenge for my people." This only made the wolves and the bear angrier. They kept on coming toward Akakapangan. He reached his kayak and pushed out from shore as hard as he could. The wolves almost caught him. They bit off part of his kayak. They even tried to swim after him, but the water soon got too deep for the wolves, so they returned to the shore and watched him go off home.

As the boy was going home he thought to himself, "Oh, how wonderful! My people will no longer be afraid to go out hunting." Soon he arrived home, where his grandmother and the wealthy couple were waiting for him. They greeted him with joy and made him a meal, and later he told them about his adventure. The wealthy man was so amazed he offered the boy one of his daughters to be his wife. Akakapangan said, "Oh, thank you!" and the grandmother said she was very thankful too. She told her grandson to be a good son-in-law and to look after his wife with care. "Yes," said Akakapangan. So he thanked the wealthy man for his consideration, and he assured his grandmother that all her teachings would help him in his new life with a wife to care for. He settled down to look after his wife and the grandmother who had raised him since childhood.

A Man Called Ekinelik

Ekinelik lived with his family, but in his own separate home. He would go out hunting seals, and whenever he got one, he would bring it back home and let his sister cut up his catch. One day he returned home from hunting to tell how he had almost caught a walrus, but lost it in the end. How Ekinelik lost a walrus became a favourite joke in the village. Some said that if he was a better hunter, he would have managed to catch the large walrus.

Soon Ekinelik got tired of people picking on him about the walrus he had lost. He said to them, "I will get a walrus yet. You'll see!" They just laughed at him. But he kept going out hunting until eventually he brought home a walrus.

Everyone in the encampment was very happy. They used every part of the walrus carcass; they never threw anything away, keeping the blood for making special broth, freezing the meat to keep it fresh, and saving the tusk for carving.

Ekinelik had a brother, who went caribou hunting but never returned home. After that, whenever Ekinelik hunted caribou, he looked for his brother at the same time. One day when he was out hunting, Ekinelik reached the area where his brother was lost. He climbed to the top of a small hill, all the while thinking of his brother.

From the top of the hill, he saw a large group of caribou emerging from a valley below. One of them was very white, like an arctic

NANOGAK

hare. Ekinelik started to stalk the caribou, and the white caribou was the one he particularly wanted. He shot it, but as he ran up to it, he saw that it was really his lost brother, who had turned into a caribou. He cried for his brother, but it was too late; he had killed him and there was nothing he could do but grieve for him. Later, he cut up the caribou and carefully dried the meat and the bones.

After his grief had subsided, he went home, taking with him every piece of the meat he had dried and every piece of bone. Back home, he put these remains away, along with the white hide.

Soon after, Ekinelik took a walk up in the hills. He heard calling and saw that the sounds came from two large birds. One of the birds flew up and landed near Ekinelik, and said to him, "I have lost our child. I have looked for him, but cannot find him. Can you help me?" So Ekinelik said, "I too am grieving. I lost my brother, and killed him because he had become a white caribou. I have suffered very much. I just recently started to hunt again. I advise you to take care in case you come across your child as something else. I will look out for him, and I will ask around for you, and if I find him, I will let you know."

So Ekinelik went on his way home to his people. They were near the shore, so when fall arrived, they started to go ice fishing. One day Ekinelik was fishing through a hole in the ice, when down near the bottom he saw a red char dancing, using the side of its cheek for a drum and one rib for beating on the drum. Ekinelik watched for a while; then he shouted to the char, "Hey, what are you doing?" The char was startled. It put its cheek and its rib back in place and swam away.

A short time later a seal swam under the fish hook. He too started a dance, using his shoulder blade as his drum and a rib for beating on the drum. Ekinelik watched for a while, until he tired of it and said, "Hey, why are you dancing?" The seal said in reply, "The char danced, so I decided I should do a dance also," and then he too swam away.

Ekinelik was still fishing a little while later, when a sculpin fish arrived below the hole in the ice. She too started a dance. Ekinelik said, "What is your name? "My name is Ayanga yan," answered the sculpin fish. Ekinelik liked that name very much. He started for home, saying the name over and over on his journey. "Ayangayan! Ayangayan!" he repeated. But he was concentrating so much on the name that he did not pay attention to his way home, and along the way he froze to death. Next day, his people got very worried when he did not come home, so they went looking for him. They found him frozen by the wayside, looking as if he was in the middle of talking.

The people prepared a grave for Ekinelik, and they buried him. Just as they finished, a blizzard blew up, and it was windy for days after. After the winds died down, the people then resumed their normal lives.

III Tales of Sorrow and Revenge

The Old Man's Son, The Whale

There was a couple living on the sea coast who had no children. The man was a hunter and a very good hunter at that. He had never returned home empty-handed. The couple were very happy together. They always had plenty to eat and they never went short of meat; they had lots of caribou and seals and other game. When the man went out hunting his wife would stay home. They were very isolated. Nobody lived close to them and nobody ever came to their place. This was the way they had lived for a long time.

All of a sudden, the wife's attitude began to change. She stopped being happy to see her husband when he returned home from hunting. She began to be quiet towards her man, not saying anything to him. Sometimes her husband tried to cheer her up, but it was no use; she wouldn't smile and laugh. He would tell her of the times he was out hunting when he was successful in getting this animal or that. He tried everything to make her happy, but he failed. She wasn't really watching her husband when he returned home from hunting, although she prepared his meals and clothing and did everything required of a wife. But she was sad. Her husband began to wonder what had become of his wife. Why wouldn't she be happy?

The man was sure that his wife was not going to change. One morning he got ready to go out hunting again, and he left the house just before dawn. But he did not go far. Just a little distance from the house, he lay down on his belly, waiting for daylight to come. His wife did not know he was there. He lay there hiding, waiting for daylight to come. He was thinking, "Why is my wife not happy with me? What has happened to her?" Daylight came, it was bright, and he still was lying there. Finally, his wife came out of the house. She had in her hand sinews made for sewing. She went up on the roof of her house and sat down, looking out towards the sea. Always looking towards the water, she started singing and waving her hands with the sinews. I have forgotten the words of the song, but she wanted someone to come to her. While she was doing this, something became visible out on the sea — a big bowhead whale was now coming towards her, bobbing up and down in the water. Her husband could see her still singing her song and waving her arms as the whale came closer and closer towards her. Finally the whale reached the shore in front of her house.

As the whale beached on the shore, out of the whale's breathing hole leaped a young man, handsome and agile. The young man went up to the woman's house and she took him inside. After some time in the house, they both came out again. All this time, the husband was watching them from a distance, but they didn't know it. The young man went to the whale and entered again by the breathing hole, and the whale went out to sea in the same direction from which it had come. When the whale was a long way out, the woman went back into the house. And when the whale was out of sight, her husband started for home.

When he got home, his wife did not pay much attention to him, as usual. He went outside and started to look for long sticks, saying to his wife, "I have seen some really big wildlife and I am going to make weapons to use in hunting it."

He set to work to make a very large harpoon, a weapon to kill the animal he had seen. Soon he finished his new weapon. He was now ready to deal with the animal and he waited impatiently for morning. Next day, he got up very early, and took his new weapon and went out, telling his wife that he had seen an animal to kill. His wife did not seem to care; she only bowed her head, sad.

The man walked out not very far from the house and waited for daylight. When the sky got brighter, his wife came out of the house with her sewing sinews in her hand and went onto the roof and started to sing and wave her hands as she had before. Soon she saw a whale coming, bobbing up and down in the water out at sea. Closer and closer it came, the woman still singing and waving her hands. Just as before, the whale beached right on the shore in front of the house and the young man leaped out of its breathing hole and jumped onto the beach, landing on his feet. The young man went up to the woman and she took him into her house. As soon as they had gone inside, the husband ran as fast as he could, clutching his weapon, down to the whale. No sooner had he reached it than he began to harpoon it again and again. Right then the young man ran out of the house towards the whale, but as he reached it and was about to go inside the whale, he fell dead and lifeless.

The wife came out of her house and saw that her husband had killed a whale. She was very happy and excited. Right away she started cutting up the whale. Both of them cleaned it and cut up and put away the meat, burying some in gravel and storing some on meat racks. After they had finished cutting it all up, they cleaned up the area where they had made a mess, turning the rocks over to their clean sides. Every rock was turned until there was no trace of blood or oil. The whole area looked very clean. Then they both sat down to rest. The wife was very happy now, no longer angry with her husband.

While they were both sitting and resting, two kayaks came in sight out on the sea. Both kayaks were being paddled towards them from the very same direction that the whale had come from. As the kayaks drew near, the couple saw that they were paddled by an old man and an old woman. When the kayaks were close, the old man shouted to them, "Do you know if our son has ever come to this place?" They replied, "No, we have never seen him; no one has ever come to us from down there!" they both lied. But again the old man was persistent and said, "Here is his trail. We have followed his tracks and they led us to this very spot." The couple lied again, saying that they did not know him.

The old man and the old woman would not give up. They said, "You must tell us or we might do this" — and at that moment the ground almost tipped over! The old man said, "Surely you have seen him. We won't hurt you, but you must tell us the truth. If you have taken him as a whale, all you have to do is tell us." Even though the couple heard the old man, they started to lie again as before. Because they couldn't tell the truth, the old man and old woman turned their paddles over, and suddenly the whole land turned over too. The whale meat and muktuk floated up in the water. The old man said, "See, you have both been trying to lie to us. You see, your meat and muktuk is our son." Then the old man and the old woman went back out to sea again.

Avaotok

This is a true story, told to us by my grandmother Mamie Mamayook. It became a legend and many knew of it.

Long ago there was a man named Avaotok, a strong man, a good hunter, a good athlete. In those days, if you were good at hunting or stronger than other men, the others tried to fight you or even kill you, because they envied you.

Avaotok lived with his family away from the rest of the people, in a house some distance from his community.

When fall came, polar bears sometimes roamed into his camp. One evening, while it was about time to sleep, Avaotok's dogs started to howl once in a while. When it got dark, they really started barking.

Avaotok was very brave and very strong. He knew that a polar bear had arrived in his camp. He went outside, and though he didn't see anything, he had his bow and arrows and he had his double-edged knife with him. He waited, but nothing was to be seen. At daylight, all of a sudden the bear appeared and Avaotok killed it.

Avaotok had two wives, and together they sharpened their ulus and knives. They went out to skin the bear, but when they opened its belly, they found it was not a bear. It was a bear skin that had been filled or stuffed with wood shavings, and its insides were made of braided sinew attached to its mouth and tongue.

Avaotok knew that the people of his community had made this bear to hurt him, and he began to feel angry at the people. They were always against him, because he was a mighty man.

Avaotok had been prepared by his grandparents as a child, so that even if he was shot with an arrow, he would not have a wound in his body. If the arrow was pulled out of him, the place where the arrow had entered would heal instantly. He had a cousin who was protected in the same manner. Only this cousin could wound him, and no-one else, and he was the only one who could wound his cousin. This was a traditional way that our forefathers used to fix their people long ago. Those whom they favoured and loved, they would make like that.

Avaotok was very angry because the people had tried to kill him, and he went to the settlement to revenge their action. When he reached the houses at the edge of the village, he rushed onto the first roof, and slashed the window, which was made of light skin from whales or seals. When the window was opened, the house was filled with cold air, and steam, and the people inside came running out.

Avaotok started to kill the people one by one as they came out of the house. Then he looked inside and he saw a little boy who was left alone with those who were sick and unable to get out. Even though they pleaded, he killed the sick people without mercy. The one little boy, though, he could not catch. He would miss him every time, because the boy would turn into a weasel and escape out of his hands, only then to become a boy again. The boy got out of the house and escaped.

When Avaotok left the house, someone jumped him from behind, and stuck a knife in his kidneys, and Avaotok also grabbed his knife and stuck it in his opponent's body. When he turned around to see who it was, it was his cousin, so both of them were fatally wounded.

NANOQAK

They still had the strength to go home, so Avaotok plugged his side with one of his mitts, and when he got home, his people began to fix him so that he might live. Avaotok began to get well, but he said that if his cousin died, he would die also.

Every morning when they got up, he would tell his people to go over to his cousin's place to see how he was making out. They told him, "Your cousin is slowly recovering," so Avaotok said he would do the same. As time went on, the people started to say among themselves that maybe if the two men got well, they would cause a big war between the people. So one morning, when Avaotok told them to go see his cousin again to see how he was doing, they told him his cousin had died. So Avaotok said, "If my cousin has died, then I will die also." So the next day, as he said, Avaotok died too.

Then, when his cousin heard of Avaotok's death, he too died, so they were both now dead. After some time had passed and the grave of Avaotok became overgrown with grass and soil, one man whom Avaotok had wounded came across his grave. The man hated Avaotok and began to damage the grave. He then left the grave and walked towards the mainland where there are trees. While he was walking among the trees, all of a sudden a tree fell on him, and then a brown bear started to maul him. He barely made it through, but the people healed him, and he recovered.

Afterwards, the man would always tell the people not to try to do anything against those who have died, even though you have a grudge against them, because the dead have a way of revenge.

Kopilgok (Worms)

A man and his wife lived on the shore near the ocean. They had children, and the man went hunting once in a while, and his wife sewed the family's clothing.

One day the wife was cutting up a seal and her brother-in-law was teasing her. She was getting annoyed at his teasing, so she thought she would give him a scare. She struck at him with her ulu, the knife she used in her work. But she split him right in half. She was now very afraid of her husband, so she hid the body where her husband would not be able to find it

A few days later the husband asked his wife where his brother was: "Why doesn't he come home?" The woman said she did not know why he did not come home. But one morning the husband went hunting and found his brother's body. Only then did the wife admit she had killed him. The husband was very angry, and he went hunting caribou to calm down.

It was springtime already, and the caribou he got had started to get worms called Kopilgok. The husband dug a big ditch and dropped the caribou into it. From then on, as summer approached, every time he went hunting and caught caribou he would drop them into the big ditch. Soon the kopilgok were very large, because the husband always dropped the caribou into the ditch, and the noise of the kopilgok could be heard very far off.

One day, while the husband was out hunting, the wife saw a lem-

ming come to her doorway and she gave it some food. Each day after that the lemming would come for a free meal. This lemming told the wife that the husband was raising kopilgok in great numbers in order to feed her to them. The lemming said, "You should sew a very pretty parka made with pretty fringes on it, because it will be the only way you will get to free yourself from the death plot your husband is setting up for you. When your husband starts to throw you to the kopilgok, run and throw the parka up in the air and then put it on as it comes down."

So the wife started sewing herself a parka as the lemming had instructed her, including the fringes to be sewn on the bottom.

Finally, one day the husband said to the wife, "Let's go for a walk." While they were walking, the wife asked, "What is that noise? Where is it coming from?" The husband told her, "Soon you will see." They were getting closer to the ditch. The husband got another caribou while they were walking, and told his wife to help him. She helped him as she was told. They both dragged the caribou to the kopilgok. When they dropped the caribou down into the ditch, it was eaten up in no time because the kopilgok had grown very large. The husband told his wife, "That is how they will eat you up for letting me suffer over my brother's death!" and he started chasing his wife around the ditch. Then the wife remembered the lemming's instructions. She threw her parka up in the air and put it on as it came back down, and the husband fell into the ditch of kopilgok. He had raised them to kill his wife, but instead they killed him. The wife turned into a wolverine and went on her way.

The Wealthy Man's Daughter

A wealthy couple lived at the seaside. They had many children who were grown up and married, but one of their daughters had never wanted to marry. She never found anyone she liked to be her husband.

One day, her father brought her another suitor. "Look," he said, "Here is someone nice for you. He is a good hunter." But the daughter got angry and refused to marry him. The boy who was refused was very sad. For many, many days, he lay there thinking about it.

Then the wealthy man said, "It is time for us to move to a new camp." So he got ready to move, gathering all the people from the camp, pulling down the tents, and getting everything together. But the rejected boy was still very sad and refused to move with the others from the camp. He stayed behind alone.

After the people had left for a new camping area, the boy started to collect all the old clothing that had been left behind at the old camp. He gathered up the old clothes and buried them in the snow, singing an old song as he did so. As he sang, the old clothes took form and became a very handsome man. Then the two of them followed the wealthy man to the new camp.

When they reached the camp, they were invited into the rich man's home and offered a meal. Now when she saw the handsome man, for the first time the unmarried daughter thought that she had found someone she might want to marry. She asked him to sit beside her and started to give him looks to entice him to sit closer to her. So he helped himself to some food and he sat down beside her. It was very warm inside for the young man who was made of clothes, and he started to sweat. Soon he was dripping water from his face. The rejected boy was trying very hard not to laugh, for he had played a trick on the girl who had refused him.

Soon it was too hot for the handsome young man to bear, so he said, "I have to go" and ran outside. The girl ran out after him, saying, "I want to go with you." "No, you cannot come with me," he called back, but the girl followed anyway.

As she ran after the young man she had fallen in love with, she began to find old mitts, old pants, and old mukluks. But she didn't find the handsome young man, even though she tried hard to track him down. As he ran, the handsome young man had discarded himself piece by piece, since he was actually made from old clothing.

Soon the girl was lost. She began to cry out for someone to help her, but none could hear her cries. She lay down to rest, crying for her family. Then the boy she had refused came up. He had followed them. He tapped her on the shoulder. She looked up and said, "I'll go with you." But he said, "No, you can't go home with me; you'll only leave me when you get home. Follow your tracks and you will reach home."

The Boys and the Polar Bear

So the boy went another way and reached a camping place where there were some families staying. He joined them. They would go hunting ptarmigan and sometimes they would get lots.

One day, three of them were out hunting. They came across large tracks, a polar bear's tracks. The boy followed its trail. At the other end, the polar bear was waiting. When the boy got close enough he took a shot and hit the bear in the paw. The bear got very angry and charged the boy and broke all his arrows. The boy ran away. He came to a small house and went inside. The bear followed soon after. It tried to push the house down, and finally succeeded. The boy ran out and again the bear chased him. The boy was very tired and could hardly run anymore, but the bear was tired too. It was about to turn away. Then the boy climbed a large rock and the polar bear saw him and started to chase him again.

In the meantime, the other two boys got worried and began to look for their friend. Just as the bear was about to catch him, the other two boys came to his rescue. They were running as fast as they could and started to shoot their arrows at the bear just as he was about to knock over the rock that the boy was standing on. When it was over they were all very tired and so they went home to rest.

The Doll Man

One day the boy came upon an old camping place. He was all alone,
since he used to hunt that way. The camping place had been left
some time before; even the old dumping places had started to melt
from the warm spring sun. Suddenly, he saw a figure, a boy's figure,
made from a piece of hide or sealskin. It was a little girl's doll that
had become a person when the wind blew on it. The doll had become alive. The doll got up and walked toward the young man, who
said to the doll, "Come, follow me." The doll repeated his words.
Again, he said, "When I go over there, follow me." Soon he realized
that because it was a doll it didn't know how to talk, but just repeated
what it heard. So he became a little angry with it, and shot at it with
an arrow. The arrow went right through its little chest. Then the doll
did the same thing — he took the young man's bow and arrow and
shot the boy through the chest and killed him.

The doll began to follow the boy's trail. The doll reached the end
of the trail and came to the other two boys, who asked the doll man,
"Where did you come from?" The doll man just repeated the boys'
words. Again they questioned him, "Where's the boy who came from
here?" Again the doll man repeated the very same words. Then the
boys said, "This boy can't speak for himself — he just copies what
he hears." They invited the doll to come in and have a meal.

At first, whatever that doll heard, it repeated. But sometime later
the doll learned to talk for itself and started to understand what
people were saying; slowly it became a human being. Soon the doll

man was also the very best hunter around and very strong.

When springtime arrived the boys went out across the land. They would cross small rivers while fishing. Sometimes this doll man would help the other boys across these rivers, sometimes even carrying them. One day they came to a camp with many people, and everyone challenged this doll man, but he won every time. If they had to cross very dangerous, moving ice, the doll man managed with no difficulty, always taking care of the boys. There was never anything too hard for him to handle.

Many girls liked the doll man, but he never cared for them, until one day he finally found a girl he liked and took her for his wife. He decided to build a house for his wife in a place with trees. He was so strong he could just push down the trees to make logs for his house, while the other boys had to use their axes to chop down the trees. They were always amazed by their friend's strength.

Long ago there had been another doll man who was also strong, so strong that everyone was afraid. He used to search along the shore for birch bark. He would carve it into small fish, and then let the fish swim out to the ocean. But all the seagulls would come and swoop these out of the water.

One day he was tired and went home to rest. He was all alone and about to eat, when he heard someone outside his tent. A girl said, "Can I come in?" The man said, "Who are you?" The girl replied, "Thank you for giving us all those fish. When we were hungry you always fed us well. Could you come for a meal at our tent?" So he followed her to her home, and as he walked he thought to himself,

"Could this girl have come from all those seagulls that swoop up all the wood carvings that always turn into fish and swim out to the ocean?"

The girl said to him, "My father wants to thank you for all the good fish — and fat ones at that — that you have provided us. My father says you are kind."

They came to the shore, and soon he could make out a big tent. Near the tent was an older couple who were dressed in beautiful clothes, and outside the tent were rows and rows of dried fish and dried meat. They all sat down to eat. The doll man had not realized how hungry he was. He ate and ate, until he was full.

The man who had invited him said to him, "Whenever you are hungry, I will send my daughter out to pick you up and she will bring you back to your home each time you're done," and when the doll man was going home he was given gifts of food to take with him.

Four Young Girls Looking for Husbands and Other Tales

Four young girls who were looking for husbands were out fishing. One of them caught a fish with very large fins. This was the type of fish that was favoured; if any other type of fish was caught, it was discarded. The girl who had caught the fish went home, taking her catch home with her.

The other three girls stayed fishing. Evening was approaching, and still the three girls had not caught anything. They began to get very cold and were starting to think of heading home. They were unhappy, murmuring among themselves, and were jealous of the other girl, who had landed her fish early in the morning. Then one of them caught a fish with large fins and, very thankful, she took her fish home.

The other two girls had still not yet caught their favoured fish. Towards evening, one of them got a very strong bite on her hook. She thought it was the kind of fish she wanted, and she pulled her hook up. At the end of her line was a sculpin fish, with many spots on its belly. She took the sculpin fish off her hook, and said to it, "Why in the world did you get caught on my hook? You look so ugly! Go back in the water, and don't get hooked on my hook again!"

So the two girls returned home without their favoured fish. They were spending their evening at home as usual, when they heard someone in the doorway. There at the entrance was a very handsome boy, wearing a very fancy beaver-skin parka. He put his head through the doorway, and the two girls called, "Come in! Come in!" so the boy looked at the girl who had had a sculpin on her hook, and began to tease her: "You had me on your hook but did not like my looks. You sent me back down into the water, so good-bye!" Then he ran out of the house where these two girls were.

The girls were now very sorry. The boy was so handsome! The next day they again went fishing. But they never caught any more fish.

The Baby and the Fox

The large fish that the first two girls had brought home had turned into handsome men, and the two girls married them and started to have children. The first girl had a little baby boy, and then they left their home and went inland, up towards the river. Then the younger girl had a baby girl. The two children became playmates.

Whenever there was a dance at the large tent of their camp, the two young women would go out, letting the grandmother look after the children. One time, the little boy was crying for his mother and father and did not want them to go, but they left anyway. The grandmother tried to get the baby to sleep, singing to him. Later on in the evening, a woman came by and told the grandmother, "I have come to pick up the boy. His mother wants him." The grandmother did not believe her. She said, "Why would she want him? She never asked for him when she went before." She was reluctant to hand him over, but the woman persisted so much, she put the boy on the woman's back.

Later, the mother and father came home from the dance. "Where is my son?" asked the mother. The grandmother replied, "I thought you sent for him, so I gave him over to a woman. She packed him on her back and put him to sleep. She said she was going to bring him to you." "No! No!" said the mother, "You know very well I don't keep him with me when I go dancing!" The parents ran outside to check for footprints, but it was already too dark. They decided to wait until morning.

As soon as there was enough daylight, the parents set out, searching the ground for footprints. They found a one-sided print, and a little further on the one-sided prints changed into the footprints of a fox. They tracked it down and came to a den. Listening very quietly, they could hear their baby crying, down inside the den, and also sounds of people down there drum-dancing, trying to coo the baby to stop his crying. But the baby kept crying from fear.

As soon as the dancing brought the baby close to the doorway, the father grabbed him and gave him to the mother. Then they ran home as fast as they could, taking turns carrying the baby.

When they reached home, they were told never to give the baby boy any recently melted water. Also, when he first walked, they were not to let him walk on the floor.

The Squirrel Woman

Soon the baby boy grew up and became a good hunter. He always got enough meat. He was so good a provider that he had no trouble in being taken as a son-in-law. So now he had his own wife and home, and already he had one little baby boy. The grandparents always liked to look after their grandson.

One day the man went hunting near the mouth of a long river, travelling by kayak. As he drew near some cliffs, a woman called to him from a cliff, "Paddle three or four times without opening your eyes." He obeyed; he paddled three or four times, which brought him to the shore. When he opened his eyes, he realized where he was.

Again, the woman's voice called to him. "Up there is my house, inside that tree. Come, I will feed you a good meal." Again, he obeyed. He sat down inside the woman's house, and she fed him. Then the woman said to him, "You will be my husband." He told her, "I have a wife already." But she kept saying, "You will be my husband."

So he stayed. Not knowing where this woman had put his kayak, he could not leave. He stayed home, and the woman would go out to get caribou, or fish. Whenever she came home, she had either berries, or something she had caught. He wondered how she got the animals.

In the meantime, his joints were getting very stiff because he did not go out hunting.

One day when she was out, he started to wonder, "Where is my kayak? Where did she hide it?" While he was wondering this, a little old lady with the face of a lemming came to the doorway. She said to him: "I saw how you were pulled towards this squirrel animal. She is not a human woman; she is really a ground squirrel. She gets men, and fattens them up, and when they can't move from all their weight, then she kills them and eats them up."

"So I came to warn you," continued the lemming lady. "She is very strong, and she can travel underground. She hid your kayak way up there on top of a tree. But I will help you. Tell her you are hungry for something that she will have to go far away from here to hunt. Tomorrow, I will put your kayak down. When you get in the water you must paddle three or four times like you did when you came."

Later in the evening, when the squirrel woman came home, she seemed to be furious. "How come your lips were moving? Who did you talk to?" she demanded. He was surprised to see that she knew. He said to her, "Oh, yes! I was talking to a lemming, telling her not to come inside the house." The squirrel woman believed him.

Then he said to her, "I really want to eat muktuk, and seal meat, and walrus meat." She was very quiet for a long time. Finally, she said, "Those things you want are very far away to go and hunt." "I know," he said, "but I am tired of mainland food! I want my own type of food." So she said, "I will go and hunt these for you, but I will have to stay one full day hunting and may not return by late evening tomorrow." He told her, "That's okay. I will wait for you."

Next morning, as soon as she woke up, she went out hunting for the food her husband wanted to eat. She left very early. When she was gone, he came out and saw that his kayak was down on the ground already. He rushed down to the river bank near the cliff, launched himself and his kayak into the water, paddled three or four times, and was out on the river again. Soon he saw that he was near his own home. He paddled quickly home. His friends and his wife were very happy to see him. Everyone was well and his two children were growing.

He started to hunt for his family again and look after them, and he took good care of them. One day when he came home from hunting his wife asked him, "How come you never came home for such a long time?" He answered, "Why do you ask? I was away hunting." Then he saw the squirrel slyly advancing so, remembering the little old lady, he called aloud, "Please come and help me!" She came as a brown bear, and the bear and the squirrel fought, but somehow the squirrel won, and she chewed up the wife and the children.

He cried; for a long time he mourned.

The Deadly Old Couple

Some time later the hunter set out on another trip in his kayak to search for his two brothers, who were missing. As he approached a cliff, a woman called to him to come and have a meal. He was reluctant to go, but she insisted that he come, saying, "We won't harm you." So he went up.

At the top of the cliff there seemed to be many, many people, dressed in white fur parkas. While he was eating his meal, someone started a song. It was a little old man, and he was angry with the newcomer. Someone else said to the hunter, "Do you have anything in your kayak?" "Yes," he replied, "I have two wolf pelts." "Well, bring them up and show them to that cranky old man."

So he went down to his kayak to pick up his wolf pelts, but when he picked them up they came alive and walked towards the old man. The old man was afraid. "Please take back these wolves!" he begged. So the hunter grabbed the wolves and put them back in his kayak, where they became normal skins again. The old man said, "I will try not to be angry with you again."

Then he continued, "You know, the two you are looking for are way upriver. If you need any help we will be happy to help you, but those people up the river are dangerous. We will remember you and watch for you."

So the hunter went on his way up the river. If he turned to look back he could see seagulls over his shoulder. These were his new friends, looking out for him.

Soon he came to a house up near the narrow part of the river. He approached the house with caution. As he drew closer, he heard a dog starting to bark. It sounded like a very small dog, but still, he turned around and went back a little way downriver, before trying again. This time he left his body behind and drifted up as a very light feather.

Up the river at the house, a crane and a dog were guarding the house. The crane never saw the feather and the dog did not bark at it. He landed lightly in the porchway. When he was safely past the dog and the crane, he turned back into a man. "I am looking for my two brothers," he said. Then he saw two human heads lying on the floor, and he recognized his brothers' faces.

Up at the far end of the room, an old couple were lying on the bed, too hot to do anything. The old man said, "How did you come in?" He screamed at his dog, "Dog, how did you let him pass you?" The dog answered, "I did not hear him walk past me!" The old man screamed again, "Crane, how did you let him go past your sharp eyes?" The crane answered, "I did not see him walk across my path!"

The hunter paid no heed to this. "I have been looking for my brothers," he said, "and you have their heads out there. I want them to live!" The old man said, "I will give you one of these ulus. Which do you want?" Thinking of revenge, the hunter answered, "I want the very largest ulu you have." So the old man picked up his biggest ulu and threw it down. The hunter grabbed the ulu and hurled it towards the old man, cutting off his arm. The old man snatched the ulu and tried to cut off the hunter's head, but he missed.

Again the hunter grabbed the ulu and cut off the head of the old man. Then he did the same thing to the wife, and the crane. He went outside and cut up the house and all that had belonged to the old couple, except the dog. The dog he harnessed to a small sled that he saw, and he made the dog pull the sled towards home. But in the end he killed the dog too, because the dog had always barked at any people who came to save their kinfolk. These people were always caught because the dog and the crane had always let the old couple know if anyone came up the river. So the hunter destroyed them all.

The hunter returned home, and went back to hunting and storing meat away. Then he thought to himself, "Maybe I should look for any other people who may be around," so he travelled way up inland, until he came upon a camp where people were making dried meat. He went up to these people and told them how far he had travelled, and that he had a lot of meat stored away, which he offered to share if they needed any other type of meat. They welcomed him and he joined them for a meal. In fact, he stayed for a few days. A young girl took a liking to him; he took her for his wife and brought her back home with him.

"I will give you a home," she agreed with him. She worked on furs, like wolverine and wolf, and caribou hides, and she sewed all her clothing for herself and her husband.

But she always went out at moonlight. Night after night, as time went on, she would go outside in the moonlight. It was very strange to him.

He decided to sneak after her one night. She went out and he followed her outside. She was standing looking at her shadow, and she was singing a song that went like this: "Oh! my shadow, look so pretty…" She was going on and on, and once her husband saw what was going on he crept back inside. When she finally came back inside, he was smiling at her.

Next morning, he asked her, "What type of fur would you like?" "I would like muskrat pelts," she replied, so he said, "I will go muskrat hunting." After he had collected enough pelts, he returned home, where his wife cleaned out the muskrat pelts and, when they had dried, softened them. When that was all done, she made herself a muskrat-fur parka, and she looked beautiful, and her husband was pleased to see his wife so well dressed.

The Race

Fall came, and there was to be a foot race, to be held over a few days. Each person racing was asked, "What would you like for a prize if you win?" "I want a new parka made for my wife," said one, "made from summertime ermine and wintertime ermine." They asked him, "What would you like for trimmings?" "Please use wolverine trim," he said, "and put trimmings on the bottom of the parka."

"How about you?" they asked another person in the race. "What would you like for yourself?" "I would like for myself a summer-ermine-pelt parka, and I want good native dried meat, and for my wife I want rabbit marrow and caribou meat." Then he added, "And also for my dogs, give them reindeer milk in their dog food pot."

So each runner had his say of what he wanted for his prize. And then the race began. It lasted for quite a few days, and the runners had to camp along the route until they finished the race and there was a winner.

The day came when the runners were expected to finish. The people waited with excitement. At last, a long way off, they saw the runners coming. The hunter was the winner. He got all that he had asked for his prizes, and more. The people also gave him some carvings, and some women gave him items of clothing. And they also chose him to be their new leader.

Three Husbands

Summer came. They started their travels across the land, towards the river, and each time they stopped among other people, they would share their food with them. At one of these stops, they adopted a girl who was old enough to get a husband, but who always refused to marry the men presented to her. One day she said yes to a crow to be her new husband.

Now, meat had been disappearing from the people's caches; this crow had been stealing. Soon the people began to look for the person who stole it. They saw footprints on the ground and realized that if they could find the person whose prints matched them, they would find the thief.

So one by one they took off their mukluks and compared their footprints. No one's matched. Only that girl's husband was left. "Let us see your feet!" they demanded. The crow said, "No, my feet are the same as yours." But the leader insisted, "No! You must show your feet." They took off his mukluks. He had only three toes. His prints matched. "So you're the stealer!" The people crowded around him. "You rotten thief!" they said. "Don't you know how to hunt for yourself?" The crow got so ashamed, he flew out the window and never came back.

The people started to make fun of the girl who had married him. She cried and cried from shame. She vowed that she would never marry anyone from this camp. She said she wanted a man from another tribe, so she refused every other man who came to ask for her hand.

One of the young men the girl had rejected had a grandmother who felt sorry for him, so she plotted something. The grandmother tightened up her muscles and tightened up her whole body; she put some fish-egg cream over her old skin, which became light and young; and she turned into a young man called Koplogik. He was to take revenge for the grandson who had been refused.

So Koplogik climbed into his kayak, after dressing up very handsomely, and he paddled along the shore until he reached the girl's home. Someone saw him paddling out there, on the shoreline, and called, "Who are you?" Someone else said, "That man looks like Koplogik." The girl heard them, and she came running out to meet this handsome man. She took him as her husband. The old lady acted as if she was a young man and the girl was very pleased.

Soon after, they were asked to a dance in the big camp tent. The dance began. Koplogik was dancing with his wife, when suddenly someone shouted from outside, "Hey! Some brown bears are coming!" So the people inside the tent rushed out. As they were pushing to get outside, they trampled on the old lady who was posing as a young handsome man, for her body was old and could not move fast to get out of their way. The old woman burst and her remains scattered over the floor. She returned to her former self as an old woman.

Someone said, "Hey! What is this? This young man was really an old woman. That girl who always refused us has goofed again! Ha, ha!" They began to make fun of her, and she cried of shame as before.

Finally, she became the wife of one of the local people, Kakolik. But he soon suffered the loss of his wife, because she became ill from all the shame, and died. So her parents suffered and cried, and her husband grieved deeply.

Her husband could not recover from his mourning. So the mother started a shaman dance, singing "Kakolik loves you, my daughter! He is suffering for you!" While she was singing, something landed on top of their house. She stopped singing to listen. Something or someone was crawling out on the porch.

The mother, Kakolik's mother-in-law, said to him, "Kakolik, look out there." But he was scared and refused. So she sang again, "My daughter, Kakolik loves you! He is suffering from his loss!" Again she told him, "Kakolik, go and check out there." But though he cried for his wife, he was scared to look outside. The mother sang some more, and there at the doorway was Kakolik's wife coming in. She had crawled from her grave at the command of her mother's song.

The mother said, "Kakolik, take her!" He just stayed still, afraid. The wife was refused, so she turned around and went back to her grave.

Kakolik learned his lesson, not to mourn so much at his loss, for now he had seen some eerie ways of people coming back to life. He resumed his normal life again — hunting, storing meat, helping people out. Even though he missed his wife.

A Story of Kraomavik

Two people had just been married recently. The wife was sewing new garments for her husband, and the husband was making brand-new harnesses for his dog-team, getting ready for the winter, and also getting his hunting gear all ready to use. From the time they got married, they were always busy like this, hunting and travelling, with the wife sewing, or cooking for her husband.

One day on their travels they came to a camp called Kraomavik, which means the Month of Moonlight, November. During that month, when it is evening, they have dances, drum dances, and play Inuit games into the night.

One evening the wife's husband was dancing on the floor of the igloo, trying to receive the gift of shamanism. His gift was two women who came to him every time he started his shaman dance, and who would do what he asked them to because they were his shaman spirits. One of the spirits had a very beautiful caribou parka made of very thin summer caribou skins, and the other spirit had a slightly thicker-skinned caribou parka. The second spirit was very mean to people around her, while the first spirit would not hurt anyone. Now these two women were the man's shaman spirits, and the people around him started to talk about him and make fun of him, saying, "He is like an old man because he has shaman spirits," and yet he was just a young man.

One bright morning he set out to hunt caribou to provide meat for his wife. When he did not return home, the people in the village started to look for him. Soon they reached where he had been hunting, and there on the ground were many footprints. The tracks were going round and round all over the hunting ground, as if someone had been chased away or was running away from something. Eventually, the search party found the hunter they were looking for. They found him where he had fallen, near his dog-team, face down on the ground in the snow. "For sure," they thought, "He is dead." But when they touched him, they found he was still alive, so they brought him back to the camp.

Then one night the husband left his wife for another woman somewhere else. The wife wondered, "What did I do to cause my husband to leave me?" She vowed that she would never marry anyone else in her whole life. Sometimes she would worry about how she would get by. And every day she wondered why he had left her for another. Even though he had married another woman, the husband always sent his former wife some meat of every animal he killed. He made his new wife bring the meat to her, because he felt he still had to provide for her.

A few months passed and then the former wife realized that she was going to have a baby. "How did that happen?" she wondered. She no longer had a husband and yet she was going to have a baby. One morning her former husband came himself to bring her meat. He was surprised at her condition and he asked her the same question she asked herself so many times "How did you get pregnant?"

One morning very early she went outside her home and saw a very handsome man with very well-made clothes — his mukluks were made from wolf legs, beautiful, with very pretty trimmings, and he had on a very fine parka with wolverine trim. She realized that he was her spirit husband and that he must be the father of her baby.

Soon the baby was born to her, a beautiful son. Now she had someone to keep her company; there would be no more loneliness for her. She made new clothes for her son, doing her very best to sew the clothes beautifully, because she loved her son very much.

One day the woman decided to go to the underground ice-house to get some arctic char. Not for the first time, it seemed to her that some arctic char were missing from her meat cache. She wondered who might be stealing from her cache.

A few days later, she needed more fish, so she went again to the ice-house. As she descended, she heard a rustling sound as if there was someone present in the house. She looked up to the ceiling and there she saw two spirit people. They were looking for something to eat and they seemed afraid. So the woman told them to get some fish. The two spirit people thanked her and told her that the man she had married was their brother, so the woman told the two spirit people to take meat whenever they were short of food.

One day the woman was given a job with the whalers, sewing clothing for all the hunters. The woman also made a very special ball for the hunters; she made this with extra care because it was to be used for celebrations after every successful whale hunt.

The men hunted whales out in the open water, and when the hunters killed a whale, there was a great celebration, since everyone was thankful for their catch. The whole camp — mothers, children and all — would celebrate the harvest.

After one such successful whale hunt in which they had killed many whales, after they had cut up the whale meat and put it away, the hunters started to play football with the special ball made by the woman's hand. But somehow another tribe had stolen their ball and replaced it with another, which started to jump all over the place as if there was an evil spirit inside. The other tribe was trying to harm the successful hunters because they were jealous.

Fortunately, one elder in the hunters' camp was a wise old man. He gave his grandson his very own knife, which he usually kept in his sleeping roll or on his person, and he said to his grandson, "When that jumping ball comes near you, I want you to place your self underneath it and give it a very sharp slice." As the ball bounced toward him, the grandson did as he had been told by his grandfather. As the ball came down, the boy sliced it, and out of the ball came an old fish net, which must have been stuffed by the jealous tribe into the ball.

An old man shaman was responsible for this and other evil schemes against the whalers. On one occasion he even put a stuffed wolf hide made to look like a real live wolf into the big igloo where they held all their celebrations. This was one of the old man's schemes against the whalers. He wanted to do this because their old men were not getting the choice part of the whale meat, particularly the flippers, which are a delicacy. So the people in the village would no longer allow him to come to the community.

Springtime came and they started to hunt whales again. One day they found what seemed to be a whale floating in the open water. A few of the hunters brought some of it home. They ate a little and then they started to die, because what they ate was not a whale but a giant sleeping while it was floating. From then on they did not bring home anything that they did not kill themselves.

One day they went hunting again out on the ice. A big wind came up, and the ice they were hunting on started to float away. Soon they were in open water, drifting farther and farther away from their own hunting grounds. They cried out as loudly as they could but no one heard them. After a very long time they finally returned to what seemed to be their own camp, to find that their wives had new husbands and children, but the hunters who returned were happy just to come back home.

The man who had left his first wife gave up his second wife because he had learned about an eagle spirit and wished to become like it. He told his second wife that he could now fly right over the great open water to visit his first wife, but she refused to believe his story. So he decided to show her how he had learned to fly. First he told her to tie up his hands behind his back, then to put rocks as weights to make his body heavy. Then he turned into an eagle and was still able to fly across over the open water. When he had returned to his first wife, she asked him, "Why didn't you come back to me when you realized you could easily get around now that you could fly?" He answered, "I did not want to leave my new belongings behind." His first wife could not understand him but he insisted that his belongings meant that much to him.

Atangnak

Once there was a man called Atangnak. Most people didn't like him because of something he had once done to them. So one day a group of men got together and they had arrows and spears, and they started to hunt for him.

They came to a group of families, and one of the hunting party called out towards a tent, "Is there a man called Atangnak in there?" Someone answered, "Yes, he is in here, but he is unable to fight. He can barely move." But the hunters kept calling his name, telling him to come out.

All this time Atangnak was inside the tent making sure his bow-string was tight, so that when he started to use it, it would be strong. Someone shouted out, "Atangnak is coming out to fight with you." Atangnak started outside with his bow and arrow.

All the men who had come to challenge him started to shoot their arrows at him, but every time an arrow came at him he would grab it out of the air. Soon his opponents had no more arrows left, yet not one arrow had hit him. When his opponents had run out of arrows, Atangnak started to shoot their arrows back at them. One by one the men were shot dead. Only one man was spared so that he could go back to his home and tell of this.

From all of the arrows that had been shot at him, Atangnak's parka tail was worn out and almost completely shot off. He waited for a while, but no one else came to challenge him, so he went home. Night came and he went to bed. But he remained alert. He was feeling very cautious about the situation he was in, and he was on his guard because some enemy might come and challenge him anytime.

When his dogs began barking, Atangnak thought to himself that his enemies had come. He began to get dressed and he told his children not to go out. But while he was still putting on his mukluks, all of a sudden a polar bear's head appeared at the entrance of the house. There was some seal meat that Atangnak was thawing out near the entrance, and the bear grabbed it in its mouth and started out backwards. Atangnak went right out after the bear but, going out of the porch, he tripped and fell right on the bear's chest. Strangely, the bear did not bite him. Atangnak was a man of the kind that no animal or nothing with teeth would try to bite him. So because of this the bear was afraid of him and turned to run away. Atangnak was right behind the bear. As soon as he could grab his bow and arrow, he shot it.

So Atangnak got a bear. Soon they had it skinned. It was a fat bear. They cooked the bear meat and were eating it for some time. Atangnak's two wives stretched the bear skin on the ground to dry it. But they still always had to be very cautious because of their enemies who like to war against each other. Finally, because he was tired of feeling this way, Atangnak took both of his wives away to safety.

Atangnak's wives used to make clothes for him. He was a very large man, and his wives used to use four young calf-skins to make him a parka. Though he was a big man, he was a peaceful man. He did not fight others because of his size, but other men hated him, partly because he was successful in whatever he did and partly because of his size. They envied him. Sometimes they tried to kill him, but they would always lose.

Yet Atangnak ignored their hatred towards him. He liked the people with all his heart. Whenever they were short of meat, he would send his wives with meat for them, even though they hated him. The people came to regard him as a leader, because whenever they were short of food they always got supplies from him. He always took pity on the poor and on orphans.

Kayaoyani, the Man in a Kayak

Once, long ago, some people lived by a river where they hunted seals and fished for char. Sometimes they would have their meals outside their tents. Then they saw a man sitting in a kayak and singing a song, going overhead in the sky. The people would shout up at him, calling him by the name of Kayaoyani (man in a kayak), but they could not get his attention. So one day a man got out his bow and arrows and took aim and shot up towards the man in the sky. His arrow went straight up to the man in the kayak. Kayaoyani started falling down to the earth very fast. The people then collected all the copper off the kayak and used the metal for blades on spears and ulus and also used it for nails.

Soon more people came by kayak, in search of the man who had been shot down. The people who had taken the copper denied ever having seen Kayaoyani, so the kayak people went back home crying for the man they had lost.

Anikniyak

A married couple lived together with the husband's younger brother, who did not have a wife. The woman looked after her brother-in-law very well, making clothes for him as well as her husband, because he always helped his older brother when he went hunting. The brother-in-law had grown up with his older brother, and now he was sort of adopted by the couple, who did not have any children.

From the beginning, the younger brother wished that they would have a child, a girl, that he could look after. He sometimes asked his older brother to have a child. He wanted to be an uncle to a little girl. After some time, the woman became pregnant. When the couple told the younger brother that they were going to have a child, he again told them that he wished that it would be a girl, because he wanted to be an uncle to a girl. But when the child was born, it was a boy. The couple started to worry, because the younger brother had said so often that he wanted the child to be a girl. So the husband said to his wife, "You should make a little girl's clothing for the child so our younger brother will not know it is a boy child. Because he wanted it to be a girl, he might do something drastic and harm him, so you should make clothes like a girl's — then he won't know it's a boy."

So it was that the younger brother thought that the child was a girl, and he was happy. He protected it, trying not to let it get hurt or anything. Soon the child was old enough to play outside. The child was still wearing a girl's clothing. When the child was beginning to walk, he began to try to catch little birds, and the uncle would help him. One day, when they were away from home chasing birds, the child went to relieve himself, and the uncle saw that he was not a girl. Only then did the uncle find out that the child was a little boy instead. When they got home, the uncle told his brother and sister-in-law that he had really thought that this child was a girl, and he asked them why, if it was a boy, they had always let him wear little girls' clothing. The couple said, "Yes, it is true. We always let him use girls' clothing because we wanted a girl too." After that, the uncle became different toward to boy child, and he left him alone.

So when it came time for them to get seals, one night the younger brother stayed up all night to make a sealskin sack. He put his young nephew in the skin capsule and set him adrift on the sea. The wind started to blow as the uncle threw his nephew away. The boy was tossed up and down on the waves. Because he had thought the child was a girl and found out it was a boy instead, the uncle let it drift away out at sea, in the sealskin sack.

So, when the parents got up, they couldn't find their youngster. They looked all over for him, but they could not find him. They even asked the younger brother where their child was, but the young man would not tell them; he said he didn't know where the child was. They looked all over. No one could help them, and they could not find their child.

The boy was still out in the sack in the sea. For a long time now he had been inside the sack made of sealskin, tossed up and down over and over again. Then, after one of the tosses, he felt like he had landed on gravel. He was happy. Now it was shallow where he was being tossed around. He thought, "I must be washed up on the beach." He could hear water washing on gravel and other gravel sounds and then he also heard someone's voice. "I have found something, I have found something!" the voice said. "I have found a sealskin." He could hear two voices crying, then, "We have found something! My sister and I have found something!" When the girls pulled the sealskin up, they noticed with surprise that something was moving inside it. They wanted to see what it was that was moving, so they went to get an ulu to cut it open. When they cut it open, they cried, "Ah! A child inside!" The child had got very dirty inside the sack all this time, and he smelled very bad! So the girls took him to the grass and wiped him with grass and cleaned him off. Then they took him into the water and washed him until he was clean. They were glad that he was a boy. The little boy told the girls that his uncle had made a sack and put him in it and let it drift away. So the girls had much pity for him and they cleaned him up very carefully.

They brought the little boy home to their father and mother. The girls were the daughters of a very rich old couple. The girls' father was a great man who was in charge of other lands; he was well-respected.

The old couple liked the boy very much. They named him Anikniyak. They wanted him to be a mighty man. They fixed him up, putting a wig on him, and dressing him in weasel-skin clothing. They fixed him up in all sorts of ways to make him look impressive. Be-

cause they had found him as a castaway, they adopted him. They loved him very much, and the two girls took him as their brother and cared for him and loved him very much.

So from this time on the boy did not suffer anymore, because he was adopted by wealthy people.

Soon it was time for the boy to begin hunting. Once he started hunting, his step-parents started having meat to eat. The boy was a good hunter. One day, he had got two eagles, one large and one small. His step-parents made clothing for him out of the eagles' skins. So, using the eagles' skins, the boy learned how to fly. He used to go hunting, using the eagle clothing, and he would always return home with caribou, or seals, or bearded seals, in his hands because he had become like an eagle. He always returned home with something, never empty-handed.

The step-parents told him, though, that even though he had been cast away at one time by his uncle, he should not take revenge or do any against his uncle. He should never bother people, even the ones who had discarded him. That is what his step-parents told him, not to be mad at those who had done this to him.

He longed to see the land he had left, so one day he took off again to see it from the air. As he was flying he began to recognize the land where he had lived as a child. He saw that the land where he was born was across the sea. He had drifted across the big ocean to his other land. He could see the old land clearly now as he flew over it. From way up he spotted a kayak on the sea, close by the area where he was born. There was a man in the kayak.

He flew down closer to the man and the kayak, studying the man very closely. He recognized the man as his uncle. All of a sudden he got very angry with his uncle. He took a dive towards him and landed on top of the kayak. He took off his hood. His uncle recognized him and said, "Oh! Nephew, you have come to me. How did you ever become like that? So this is my nephew...." The nephew said to his uncle, "You did not use to call me your nephew. You did not want me because I was a boy. You made a sack of sealskin. You put me inside the skin sack and you let me suffer. You had no pity for me, so I drifted across the big ocean. I was tossed around in the sea. At the time you did not want to call me your nephew, so what you yourself planned, you will have. You threw me away, you cast me away long ago. You have made me suffer."

With that, he put his hood quickly back on, grabbed his uncle with his claws, and took off upwards. He flew up and up, even though his uncle cried out to him, saying, "Don't do this! You're my nephew, don't take me up!" But the eagle took him higher and higher. The land became blue, he was so high up in the sky; he couldn't even recognize the land. Then the eagle let him go. The uncle started to fall with his kayak, falling down and down. The eagle let him fall, and went on, looking for caribou. But the eagle hunter found none, so he went home.

When he got home to his step-parents, he took off his eagle clothes and hung them up and went to sleep without eating. The old couple found their son different — he didn't eat and just went straight to sleep — and they wondered why. So the old man went to

NANOQAK

inspect the eagle clothes, and he noticed that one of the claws was ripped back, broken. He told his wife of his finding, that their son's claw was ripped backwards. They knew he must have done something to those he was angry with.

They waited for the boy to wake up, and when he finally did, the step-father asked him, "On what did you break your claw?" He replied, "I guess it was yesterday when I was hunting caribou. I must have broken it then." "No," said the old man, "you can't rip it doing that. You can't do that on a caribou." The boy answered, "Maybe it was when I was trying to get a very large fish." "No," said the old man, "you wouldn't do that on large fish." The boy didn't say any more. "So, I wonder, what did you break your claw on?" the old man asked again. The young man was quiet for a while and then told his step-father, "I did that on my uncle. I broke it on him." "So, you must have done something to him. I told you not to use your claws on people when I made your clothing. What did you do to your uncle?" So the boy said, "When I saw my uncle, I took him up in the sky and I let him drop from way up there." "So now I know," said the old man, "you must not do that again." The young man agreed and set off hunting again.

He had not forgotten about his real parents, and again he took off towards the land he was from. He looked over it and the grass had grown over the whole place. He recognized the place where his mother used to cut seals and other animals, but all of it was overgrown, so he returned home.

They say that this man Anikniyak was a mighty hunter, that

sometimes he even became a fish or other animal because the old couple taught him so well. This time he returned home by kayak. He did not use his eagle skins because he wanted to go by kayak down the river. Often his step-father had warned him not to go downstream, saying, "Sometimes the men there are very dangerous. They don't let anybody return. You might meet one of these dangerous men there." While he was kayaking downstream, he saw some movement telling him someone was nearby. Remembering his step-father's warnings, he returned quietly upstream before anyone saw him.

Leaving his kayak secured safely some distance upstream, he became a fish and started to swim downriver as a pike. He saw movement again. All of a sudden, a trident was thrust down on him. It struck him on the nose. He twisted and turned abruptly, so that the spear broke off, and took off towards his boat. He was very angry. Having swum a little way away, he became a man again and started back for the man who had tried to spear him. When he got near him, the man said to him, "Oh! You look like the one I was trying to spear." The man recognized him because, in his haste, he had forgotten to take off his fish mask with the trident that was broken on the side of his nose. He approached the man he was angry at, and killed him. So Anikniyak had again killed a man who had hurt him. Then he looked for the man's wife, and killed her too, and broke all their possessions, since this man had been one of the men his step-father had told him about, who did not let anyone return home.

Anikniyak went back to his kayak and continued downstream.

He came across a net and thought that it must belong to the dangerous men. He made himself look like he was a fish caught in the net, that had frozen. The next morning, the owner came to see his nets. When he found a fish trapped there, he was happy that he'd found something fresh to eat. Anikniyak still pretended to be frozen, while the man put him on his back and headed home. The man went into his house and said, "Here, I have brought something fresh." His wife was very glad, and their two grandchildren, waiting to be fed, said, "Thank you. My grandfather has something for us!" The children, too, were very glad that they had something to eat.

They placed the fish up on top of their meat rack and waited for him to thaw out. The children were eager to eat the fresh food, so they said, "When will it thaw out, granny? When will you cook it?" The grandmother said, "Tomorrow, when it is really thawed out, I will cook it." Then these people, who were so feared by others, went to sleep, along with their children. Just before they fell asleep, the two children looked at the fish that was to be their meal, and they saw the eye wink open a little. They cried, "Granny, he just about opened his eyes!" The grandmother answered, "Don't be scared, it is because there will be others behind him. Go to sleep." Again the children saw his eyes open, but then they fell asleep.

Anikniyak could see the large ulu hanging up in the porch. Also there on the porch was their watchdog. While they all slept, Anikniyak got down from the meat rack as lightly as a feather, grabbed the big ulu, and cut the heads off the sleeping victims. Then he destroyed everything, even the big ulu. He left nothing untouched.

Then he continued downstream, looking for more of the dangerous people. He saw a little house on the other side of the river and went over to it. A woman was scraping a skin outside the house. When he beached his kayak, the woman approached him at a very fast walk. She grabbed him by the hand and brought him to her house. The woman wanted him to be her husband, but he said to her, "Just a minute, okay? Wait a while." He felt a little afraid of her because while they were walking he could hear something that sounded like teeth rubbing. That had scared him, so he said, "Just a minute," he said. "I forgot something in my boat. I have to get it." He knew he had a seal's head down in his boat, the type that has teeth and will bite.

So he got the seal's head and told it it would have to fight for him. He put the seal's head inside his clothing and went back up to the house. Soon it was time to go to sleep, so he followed the woman to bed. Then he shoved the seal's head at the woman and said, "Here's your enemy!" The woman and the seal's head started fighting like dogs. There was a tremendous noise and the house cracked.

Rocks were crushing the house, and him, so Anikniyak turned into a hair and started twisting and turning up through small cracks as he headed for the little light he could see up above. Slowly he climbed out as a hair, and then he turned back into a man. He looked back where he had come from and saw that he had crept through a very small crack in the flat rocks. Whatever was left of the woman's belongings he laid waste. Then he went off and killed off the rest of the feared people, the ones from whom no one ever returned.

The Boy Who Wouldn't Listen

There was a poor lad, who visited his grandmother from time to time. He told her how Atangnak would let his wife give the boy food to eat. His grandmother said. "How kind of that man! That is why you must be kind to people, and that way people respect you."

Even though his grandmother also always told him not to go travelling all by himself, one day the boy set out on his own towards the land. Soon he saw a very big man up on a hill in the distance. This man would travel to camps and break up homes and destroy everything around. "How can we remove him from around here?" the boy wondered, as he travelled along the shore. He came to the camp of a wealthy man who had two daughters. They were waiting, ready with weapons, for this big man to arrive. Soon the big man descended on the camp, destroying houses on his way. He arrived at the wealthy man's place. But the young boy was waiting for him with a knife, and he cut off the big man's head.

The wealthy man was so happy that he gave one of his daughters to the boy to be his bride. He also gave him all the tools he needed. The young man was well off now, and his father-in-law treated him with respect.

The young wife told her father, "I will bring my husband's grand-mother into our home and invite her for a meal." She cooked different foods, including dried fish and dried meat, and the grandmother was very pleased. The grandmother said to her, "You are a very smart girl. You have a lot of skills for your age." The young girl replied, "My mother taught me very well." "I want you to teach your children well, the same way you were taught," said the grandmother. "You have made my grandson a good wife."

The Little People

The wealthy man's daughter's husband was making something out of wood, and it was very smooth and shiny. She said, "My husband can make really beautiful tools and he is a good hunter and provider." When her husband had finished, he had made very good sleds. The wife would go by dogteam on the sleds and she would go very fast, because the sleds were well made. This was the sign of a good craftsman.

One day the husband went out on the ice to look for seal breathing-holes. He heard a noise coming from somewhere around. "Look down over there!" someone said. So he followed the noise and found a bearded-seal breathing hole. He crouched down to wait for movement down in the hole. Soon he heard the sound of something slowly stirring and he got ready. He plunged his harpoon down hard and he caught the bearded seal. As he was pulling up his catch, he again heard the sound of voices. He cut out a piece of seal liver and threw it towards the place where he heard the voices. As it landed he seemed to hear a large number of people saying, "Oh, thank you for this food."

When he got home his wife started to work on the seal, cutting and storing the blubber for later use. While his wife worked, he told her what had happened, when he threw meat to the voices. His wife said, "You did well. Those voices you heard were little people, who usually go along with hunters, waiting for a hand-out, because they cannot hunt for themselves." His wife said, "Now next time you hunt caribou, you must give them some caribou meat." He said to her, "Yes, I will remember to share my catch of caribou meat with them. I will give them some part of the fat and some of the choice pieces."

When he got caribou, he gave some to these little people. He left some pieces behind at the hunting place, and again he heard them rejoicing with happiness for receiving meat. They were having a great big drum dance and feast. These small people always appreciated being offered meat or other things from other people. But if there were any who thought they did not exist or who did not like them, the little people could go against them.

One day the husband was walking along the lakeshore when he came upon someone weeping. He asked the person, "What's your problem? Is it because your parents have deserted you?" The person who was crying said to him in an adult's voice, "When your parents leave you, do you cry?" The man knew then that this wasn't a child. Again he asked, "Well, then, why are you weeping?" But he received no reply. So he left the small person. Later he realized that the reason this little person was weeping was that he thought the pond was too deep; the day was cloudy and the lake reflected the dark clouds, and the little man thought the lake was too deep.

Later on some people came upon a group of people playing ball. Out on the side was a person who seemed to be a small child, who was crying, and it was funny, because he had a beard. Someone said, "Why do you play ball if you have a beard? And stop crying!" The little person said, "I am not a child! Why do you make fun of me?" So the little man got angry. He grabbed the person who had made fun of him and threw him far away. This little person was a very strong man.

The little people were very fierce, and it was said that you should never get these little people angry or make fun of them. They lived in caves in the ground. There were always large fires where they lived. Even to this day there seem to be places out on the land where there might have been houses where these little people lived.

The Girl Who Sank in Quicksand

One day, when the children were playing hide and seek, one young girl went to hide along the lakeshore, but suddenly she started to sink. She had stepped on quicksand.

As she sank to the bottom, she started to sing a song about the sands. When she reached the bottom, she met a person, who never let her see his face, though soon he became her husband. Later on, though, when she had a baby girl, the young woman was very surprised when she found that the baby had one large eye in the middle of her forehead. A little while later, the young woman had a baby boy, and he too had one eye, in the middle of his forehead. What her husband said to her was, "That is why I haven't shown my face to you. I thought it would scare you." But she told him, "I am not scared of my children. I love them." So the man showed her his face, and she was very thankful to see him as he really was.

Some mornings, to her surprise, she found at her doorway caribou meat, seal meat, or muktuk. Someone was leaving this for her family, and she was very grateful. Soon the person who was leaving them the meat showed himself. He said that, because the one-eyed man had something to do with the weather, he was leaving them all this meat so that the weather would be good so the people could go out hunting. The woman thanked him.

One day, the one-eyed man told his wife, "You will be going back to your own people." She was reluctant to go away, but her husband said, "You must go. Your parents miss you." Remembering her father and mother, she agreed to go. The son would go with her, while the daughter was to stay with her father.

They began to prepare for the journey. The one-eyed man made a pair of sleds for his son. The woman sewed parkas and mukluks, and also mitts for the whole family. Soon they had all the work done, so the boy got his sleds ready, and he and his mother set out on their journey.

The mother and son came to an igloo. When they stopped, the people inside came out to see who had arrived. The old couple did not recognize their daughter who had come back to them, so she had to tell them who she was. Her mother said to her, "We missed you very much when you got lost. Your father became a shaman; he can now go back and forth from the spirit world. He can see only spirits and shadows. He will take us to the spirit world – you can come if you wish. Who is this boy?" "He is my son," the young woman answered and they went inside to have a meal.

Autumn came, and they set out on a journey together. They came to a place where some people seemed to be making an igloo. But these people were spirits; only their shadows could be seen, and then only at night-time; in daytime, they couldn't be seen at all. When these spirits used their dog-team, you could only see their harnesses; the dogs could not be seen either. You could hear them howling, but, like the spirit people, only at night could you see them, and then only as slight shadows.

The Lake With No End

One day, the young woman and her family set out for a lake to go fishing. On the way, her father told her a story:

"When I was young, I was told never to go near the lake, because there were very strange fish and strange animals in that lake, very large fish, and walrus and seal and rabbits. The name of the lake is the Lake With No End. My father, long ago, was fishing here, using a double string on his hook, when a fish got on the hook that was so large it broke his line. Some fish here have scales as big as a plate made from bone.

The next day, they were boating out on the lake, when he saw what seemed to be very large scales down in the water. He was scared, for his daughter and wife were in the boat too. Then he remembered what his father used to tell him about how to chase away dangerous animals. In the middle of the boat was a pail of drinking water. As he saw the scales of the fish come closer, he grabbed the pail of water and poured some over the side of the boat. When he did this, the fish swam lower.

Feeling him move behind her in the boat, his wife turned around and asked, 'What is wrong?' He realized that she might take fright if she was told, so he said, 'Oh, nothing. Just keep rowing.' She did, and when they finally reached the shore, he said, 'I have to tell you, when you turned around out there on the boat, I had just seen a great big fish. I thought you might be scared, so I had to wait till we came ashore before telling you.' She realized how afraid she would have

been, so she told her husband he had been right not to tell her.

Her husband told her, as well, that the reason some hunters don't return home after going boating is that they didn't listen to what their parents had told them in the past, and don't remember what to do when something happens to them."

The Lost Hunters

Later on the family started to go out hunting by dogteam, and spent the rest of the fall with some other families. The men would go out on the ice, waiting for seals at their breathing holes. One day while they were out, a blizzard started to blow. The father looked around for the person who had been next to him, but he could not see him through the blowing snow. He started for home, trying desperately to locate which way to go. He walked and walked through the driving snow, and, to his amazement, found he had made it home.

Next day, the winds died down a bit, so the rest of the people set out to find two hunters who had not returned home. When they walked out on the sea ice, they found there were new ice ridges because the sea ice had moved all around during the night of the blizzard. The people looked for the lost hunters, but could not find them, because the ice had swallowed them up.

So the people hired a shaman to try to find the lost hunters. They paid him a great sum — all their tools. The shaman laid out his parka and put his arm up the sleeve, feeling around for something. When he pulled his hand out, he was clutching something. He opened his fist. To the people's amazement, there in the palm of his hand lay two small people. They were the men the people were looking for. They were dead.

The shaman put the two little people back into the parka again, and he started his shaman dance, still looking for the bodies of the lost men. But after a while, the shaman said, "We cannot do anything for these two. They have drowned." The wives were mourning and the children were crying for their fathers, but nothing could be done.

The parents of the lost hunters started to look for the person who had called up the blizzard that took the lives of their sons. Each night they would put on the dogs' harnesses and search for evil shamans. One night, they felt they had found their man, so they lodged in his doorway, disguised as dogs, listening for any words of the strange blizzard that had taken place a few nights before.

While the old couple searched for their sons' enemies, their youngest son went to their summer camp to get seal oil for their lamps. When he returned he was very pale, for he had seen some evil spirits. The old man saw his son's face and said, "Oh, those shaman's people are going to bother us."

So the old man told his wife and sons and daughters to tie the dogs down securely, and to clean out the porch so nothing was on the ground. Then he took his drum, and started a dance in the middle of the floor, to summon his own spirits. Soon all the spirits came in answer to their master, and fought against the evil shaman who had taken the lives of the two hunters. They threw a rope to try to net the evil shaman, but when they pulled it in there was only some hair at the end of it, so they threw it out again. This time when they pulled it in they had the shaman at the end of the rope.

The old man stopped dancing and went out to the porch, where many people were waiting. He showed them the mukluks of the evil shaman, whom they had now got rid of. The mukluks had soles made from bearded-seal hide. All the people around the camp were very happy, saying, "Oh, isn't it wonderful! The evil shaman is dead," and they were all overjoyed. The family started to cut up the carcass of the shaman they had killed. Some people said, "Oh, how can you do that?" The old man told the people, "I killed the shaman because he hurt my family. Now I must clear away all traces of him."

The youngest son one day went out hunting. He got a wolf, which he gutted. But when he was getting ready to go back home with his catch, the wolf stood up and walked away. He went home and told his father of this strange happening. The old man said to his children, "Now, again, the evil shamans are trying to bother my family. Give me all of your catch of fur-bearing animals." The family brought out all of the pelts they had of different animals they had caught. The old man went outside, laden with furs, but when he came back he was empty-handed. The family knew he had got rid of these pelts to protect his family.

The old man began to wonder if his sister had been hurt by the evil shamans. He thought, "Maybe those shamans are bothering her. I'd better go and see her." He told his wife, "Don't try to wake me up if I seem to be asleep or dead; I will travel to my sister from outside my body."

That night his wife saw that her husband appeared to be dead, for he was not moving at all. Remembering his instructions, she put a blanket over him and did not try to wake him. Night passed into day, and it was evening before the wife saw that her husband's feet twitched. Later he woke up, smiled at her, and started telling of his journey. He had seen his sister, but she could not see him. Her son-in-law was living nearby, and she seemed all right. She was sewing clothing, so he had decided to come back before his body got too cold.

The Bear Woman

The man got very old, and he became ill. One day he said to his wife, "When I die I want to go to a good place. I don't want to go to a place where there is suffering. When I die some people may try to make you suffer; even while I was alive they used to try and mistreat our family. I never like to mistreat anyone who doesn't bother me. That is the way you should be."

Some time later, the old man died, and the children cried, but nothing could be done. It was still wintertime, so the family wrapped their father's body in skins and put his body up nearby, to wait until the ground thawed enough to bury him. His wife checked on the body regularly. One morning as the wife and some of the children were going up to check on him, they saw something blowing away from the wrappings. They thought it was just the wind swirling the snow, so they kept on walking towards the body. But when they reached the wrappings, and the wife checked to see if the body was still inside, the skins were empty. So they stopped going up to see their father's body. One morning, when the mother came out of her house, she saw tracks around the house and she realized that her husband's spirit was now protecting her family.

Now the older children were grown up; the boys had got themselves wives and had travelled to other places. But her two younger sons stayed home with her. One day she said to her two sons, "Let's go and see the place where your father's body was." She had a woman friend who helped her sometimes, and she told this friend, "While I am away, I want you to stack up the coals."

The friend warned her not to go: "There is a brown bear with two cubs out there." But the mother said, "I will become a mother bear, and my two sons will be my cubs." And so they travelled along to a new place after disguising themselves as bears.

When they got close to a camp of people, the bears could hear a man shouting. The man was called Pitichik and he had two wives. He did not like something they had done, so he was shouting at his wives, making them cry. Then he heard someone outside saying, "Brown bears out there!" Pitichik ran out with his bow and arrow. He saw the brown bears. He took aim, but just as he was about to shoot, the mother bear took her hood off and recognized Pitichik as her husband who had died. They had wrapped him in caribou skins, but his body had disappeared from the place where they were to bury him when the spring thaw came. When Pitichik saw that she was his former wife, he was very surprised and he said, "How did you know where to find me?" The wife said, "You have made me and our children suffer for a long time. We thought that you really had died. But all this time, you just wanted to move away from home, to marry another woman, you thoughtless old man! Your children suffered a great deal when they lost their only father. All this time you only wanted to please yourself!" So the mother bear and her two cubs decided among themselves to tear him apart. When Pitichik realized what they were going to do, he tried to plead with his former wife, but she could not forgive her husband for hurting her children so much. So she put her hood back on and she charged down on Pitichik and she tore him to bits. Later, when he died, she could not contain herself; she began to cry for her husband, who had given her beautiful children.

The mother bear and her two cubs turned back for home. They expected that they would change back to their normal selves as they were running along, but when they reached home they realized that they were still in the form of brown bears.

The woman friend who had stayed behind on her own had been taking it easy. She had forgotten to stack up the coals as she had been told. Now she jumped up, remembering what she was supposed to do, but it was too late. The mother bear was very angry and she said she would tear the woman apart. The woman was now very afraid. The mother brown bear did not want to tear her friend apart but she had to. So she did, but afterwards she cried again.

Now the brown bears had to live out on the land. Fall-time arrived, and the lakes began to freeze over. The mother bear saw some caribou and she told her two sons to go after them. They found it difficult to hunt, because the ice was slippery, but they kept on hunting, and soon they had enough meat to last them quite a while.

Gradually, somehow, they returned to their normal selves. The young boys learned from their mother's instructions how to make tools and weapons using the caribou leg bones and antlers, and how to make and use poles to poke through the snow looking for seal breathing-holes. The mother taught the sons all the ways of making tools as well as how to hunt.

Summer came and now it was time to hunt whales. The mother and her two sons moved near the shore. Even when the whales were still far away, the hunters could hear them coming. When a lot of whales travelled together, their skins would rub against each other and make a whistling sound that could be heard from a long way off. When there were calves with the whales, the calves would swim right alongside their mothers.

The mother who had been a bear told her sons never to kill killer whales, because they are not what the Inuit hunt. Even though groups might be travelling together, Inuit would not kill a killer whale. And if a killer whale came while Inuit were hunting blue whales, someone would give it food and it would go away. But if someone did kill a killer whale, it was very bad, for these killer whales had feelings. When a brother or sister or mother or father was killed, the killer whales would cry and take revenge on the person who had killed one of them. So Inuit were never careless when they saw killer whales around. And they were always cautious when they were hunting in the ocean, and people hunted together in groups.

NANOGAK

The Girl Who Was Adopted

An old couple who lived near the shore had a fine son. One day they were travelling along the shore, hunting, when they came to a family who had a daughter. She was not yet mature, but she was given to the old couple to become their daughter-in-law when she became old enough. All summer long the girl travelled with her new family. They walked, hunting caribou and camping along the way. Fall-time arrived, and they were busy getting their gear ready, their spears and knives, and bringing in all the dried fish and dried meat that they had stored away for winter use. The young girl would cry for her mother and father, and she would work very hard and get very tired.

Towards the end of winter, the family began to run out of meat and food for their dogs. The old couple decided to go to a camp which they knew was only a few days' journey away. They thought, however, that they might not have enough to eat, so they had to leave the young boy and the young girl behind.

The boy and the girl walked along in the trail of the old couple. Sometimes they would cry and cry, because they had nothing to eat and no shelter to rest in. When they reached the old snowhouses, where the people had chopped some meat, they would pick up bits and pieces to eat.

One day the girl was very tired and could not walk anymore. But away over the horizon they saw something moving, coming closer and closer. It was two teams of travellers. The boy and the girl were very happy. These travellers looked on the two with pity, for they were so ragged and hungry. So the travellers fed them, and took them on their sleds, and started out travelling again. Soon they stopped at a camp, and these people adopted the young boy and girl into their own family. The boy and girl grew up to be fine young people. Some time later, the old couple, the original parents, returned. The boy and the girl did not want to go back to them, but the old couple took them back anyway.

A while later, the old couple again left the girl and the young boy behind, this time with an old woman. This woman had no dog outside her house, so sometimes wolves and brown bears would come, but she was so strong that if she had to she could kill them by smashing their heads against the tree stumps. The boy and girl did not stay with her, however, since one day, when she was making a great big fire to keep away the wolves and bears, someone came to pick them up and bring them to a new camp.